Creative Crafts for Creative Hands

SOFT FURNISHINGS

CLB 4129
This edition published in 1995 by Tiger Books International PLC, London
© 1995 CLB Publishing, Godalming, Surrey
Printed and bound in Proost, N.V. Belgium
All rights reserved
ISBN 1-85501-599-4

Managing Editor: Jo Finnis
Editors: Sue Wilkinson; Geraldine Christy
Jacket and prelim design: Art of Design
Typesetting: Litho Link Ltd, Welshpool, Powys
Production: Ruth Arthur; Sally Connolly; Neil Randles; Karen Staff; Jonathan Tickner; Matthew Dale
Director of Production: Gerald Hughes

Photographers
Jacket Steve Tanner/Eaglemoss; Jacket flap Steve Tanner/Eaglemoss; Title Page Simon Page-Ritchie/Eaglemoss; 9 Louis Gaillard; 11 Ariadne Holland; 12 Louis Gaillard; 13 Steve Tanner/Eaglemoss; 14 (bl) Steve Tanner/Eaglemoss; 14(br) Graham Rae/Eaglemoss; 15 Romo Fabrics; 16 Jane Churchill; 17 Marie Claire Idees; 18 Steve Tanner/Eaglemoss; 19-20 Laura Ashley; 21 Elizabeth Whiting Associates; 23 Boys Syndication; 24 Steve Tanner/ Eaglemoss; 25 Osborne and Little; 27 Osborne and Little; 28 (t) Robert Harding Syndication/IPC Magazines; 28 (b) Anna French; 29 Sanderson; 31 Graham Rae/Eaglemoss; 32 Robert Harding Syndication/IPC Magazines ;33-36 Steve Tanner/Eaglemoss; 37-39 Simon Page-Ritchie/Eaglemoss; 40 Sanderson; 41 Simon Butcher/Eaglemoss; 43-44 Simon Butcher/Eaglemoss; 45 (r) Anna French; 45 (bl) Simon Page-Ritchie/Eaglemoss; 47 Simon Page-Ritchie/Eaglemoss; 48 Anna French; 49 Harrison Drape; 53 Jane Churchill; 54 Laura Ashley Home; 56 Laura Ashley Home; 57 Steve Tanner/Eaglemoss; 59 Steve Tanner/Eaglemoss; 60 100 Idees

Illustrators
10-12 John Hutchinson; 14-16 John Hutchinson; 18-20 John Hutchinson; 22-24 Jenny Abbott, Will Giles, Sandra Pond; 26-27 John Hutchinson; 30-32 John Hutchinson; 34-36 John Hutchinson; 38-40 John Hutchinson; 42-44 John Hutchinson; 46-48 John Hutchinson; 50-52 (t) Terry Evans; 50-52 (b) Julie-Ann Burt; 54-56 John Hutchinson; 58-60 John Hutchinson

Creative Crafts for Creative Hands

SOFT FURNISHINGS

How to make beautiful gifts and objects for the home, from basic techniques to finishing touches.

TIGER BOOKS INTERNATIONAL
LONDON

CONTENTS

Cushion collections

A home can never have too many cushions; piled high, one on top of the other, they always look comfortable and inviting. The secret when choosing fabrics for a collection like this is to select exciting fabrics all in shades of the same colour.

This vibrant blue collection, conjures up heady days at the seaside with deck-chair stripes and café checks mixed with pretty florals. Made in cotton fabrics and in the same hue of blue, the covers are linked by colour and texture.

To complement and contrast, the neutral coloured collection shown on page 11 includes ruched silk, stitched canvas, appliqué and patchwork cushions. In both collections colour is playing the linking theme. Be similarly ruthless with your fabric choice and only use those which complement each other. When making your selection, it's a good idea to carry swatches with you to match the fabric's colour and texture. Then, only when you're sure they work successfully together, should you buy.

The tab-edged cushion in blue shown here is easy to sew, and instructions for

▲ Seaside comforts
Collecting co-ordinated cushions can be most rewarding, especially if the theme extends further than a linking colour. Here, a theme is created using, woven stripes, checks and cotton textures conjuring up memories of the seaside. Try using them to create a similar effect.

making it are shown on page 12. Two more unusual cushions are shown on page 11 and details for making the appliquéd flower basket and ruched circular border are given on pages 10–11.

APPLIQUE BASKET

Materials

White fabric for the flowers (**a**)
Toning fabric for the leaves (**b**), backing panel (**D**) and cushion cover back (**e**)
Striped fabric for the basket (**c**)
Lining fabric for the cushion pad
Filling for the cushion pad
Matching sewing thread for making up
Matching zip 40cm (16in) long
Toning sewing thread for satin stitch
Tracing paper for the paper pattern
Dressmaker's carbon paper

This decorative appliqué cushion is really quite unusual, but it is surprisingly easy to make. The three fabrics are cut as colour blocks and satin-stitched in place, to outline the petal and leaf designs. The striped fabric used for the basket helps to combine colour shades and implies the texture of a real basket.

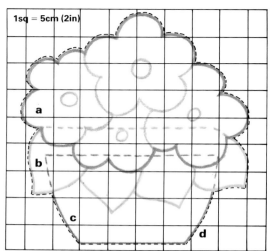

1 **Cutting out** Draw up the pattern to scale and trace off the four pattern pieces, flowers (**a**), leaves (**b**), basket (**c**) and the complete design (**d**). Cut out one of each in the appropriate fabrics and two of (**d**) in the lining fabric. Also cut two rectangles 46 x 24.5cm (18 x 9⅝in) in the backing fabric (**e**).

2 **Laying out** Place the background fabric piece (**d**) right side facing upward, on to a flat surface. Next, place the basket (**c**), then the leaves (**b**) and finally the flowers (**a**) on top, overlapping each other but with the outer edges matching. Once you are happy with the overall arrangement pin and tack in place.

RUCHED BORDER CUSHION

Materials

Decorative fabric for the cushion centre
Striped fabric for the ruched border
Plain fabric for the backing
Round cushion pad size of your choice
Matching sewing thread
Matching zip 6cm (2¼in) smaller than the diameter of the cushion pad
Iron-on interfacing to reinforce the panel
Tracing paper
Compass and pencil

The ruched border on this cushion frames an embroidery or floral fabric beautifully. Use a striped fabric for added interest to match embroidery.

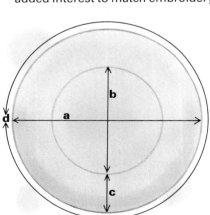

1 **Measuring up** Measure the diameter of the circular cushion pad (**a**) and decide on the diameter of the centre panel (**b**). Then measure from the central panel edge to the edge of the cushion pad (**c**) for border width. Also measure the circumference of the cushion pad (**d**).

2 **Cutting out** Using an appropriately sized plate, draw a circular pattern for the centre panel, ensuring the motif will fit in it. Add 1.5cm (⅝in) for seam allowances and cut one from the decorative fabric and one from iron-on interfacing. For the ruched border cut out a strip from the striped fabric, 3 times the circumference of the pad (**d**) by the border width measurement (**c**), adding 1.5 (⅝in) seam allowance all round. For the cushion back cut a rectangle measuring (**a**) x (**a**), adding 3cm (1¼in) to one side plus seam allowances.

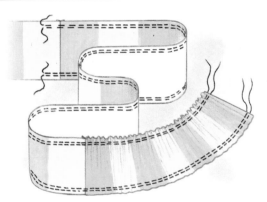

3 **Making up** Iron the interfacing on to the wrong side of centre panel. If necessary, join border pieces together to form a long strip. Run two lines of gathering stitches along each long edge, 1cm (⅜in) from each edge. Pull up gathers, easing one side to fit around the centre panel.

4 **Joining the centre** Seam together the ends of the ruched border strip and then with right sides together, pin the ruched border around the centre panel. Tack and stitch in place, ensuring the gathers are even.

5 **Making up the cushion** Cut across the back panel parallel with the short sides and insert the zip as in Applique flower basket *see step 5*. Next, measure and cut out a circular pattern, matching the cushion pad's dimensions, adding 1.5cm (⅝in) for seam allowance. Cut out the cushion back. With right sides facing, tack and stitch the cushion back to the ruched border, ensuring the gathers are even. Turn to right sides through zip opening and insert cushion pad.

▶ *Cool beige collection*
A wonderful array of natural colours combined in many different tones, textures and designs. Even the techniques used to create the cushions are widely varied.

5 Inserting the zip Tack fabric pieces (**e**), together forming a square, 46cm (18in). Centre the zip right side down, with the teeth directly over the seam. Tack then machine stitch the zip in place.

3 Transferring the design Placing the traced pattern on to the fabric pieces, mark on the flower and leaf outlines, using either carbon paper or tack through the paper. Cut four irregular circles, between 2-2.5cm (¾-1in) in diameter for the flower centres. Pin and tack in place.

4 Defining the foliage Using a toning thread and satin stitch, start stitching the design in the order given. Each line of stitching should overlap the ends of the previous one. Start at the lower right leaf detail and work across to the left. Continue with the lower flower, the flowers on either side, then finish with the top flower and the centres.

6 Shaping the cushion back Place pattern (**d**) over the cushion back (**e**) and cut to shape. Then with wrong sides together, pin and tack the appliqué front to the cushion back around the edges.

7 Making the cover Carefully satin stitch around the edge of the cover, joining the front and back panels together and neatening the raw edges at the same time.

8 Making the pad With right sides together, stitch the two lining pieces together leaving an opening in the lower edge. Trim seam allowance to shape and turn to right sides. Fill the pad with wadding before sewing the opening closed. Insert the pad through the zip opening of the cover and adjust to fit.

tip

Stitching away
If your machine has no facility for satin stitch, stitch the design by hand. You could also embroider the flowers.

CHECKS 'N' TABS

Materials

Main fabric blue and ecru check for the cushion
Toning fabric blue and ecru stripe for the tabs
Matching zip 5cm (2in) shorter than cushion pad width
Matching thread
Cushion pad the size of your choice
Squared paper, **pencil** and **ruler** to make the pattern

This country check cushion is an effective way of using two different fabrics in the same colour, without making the result too loud to live with. It is very easy to make-up, the tabs are simply inserted at regular intervals around the outside seam.

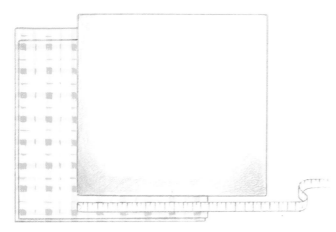

1 Cutting out Measure your cushion pad and draw up a pattern to the same dimensions adding 1.5cm (⅝in) seam allowance all around. Cut one for the front piece then add a further 3cm (1⅜in) along one side to make a rectangle and cut out one piece for the back piece. From the toning fabric cut sixteen pieces, 10 x 5cm (4 x 2in) for the tabs.

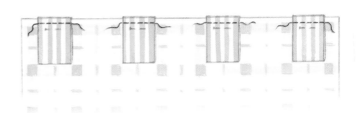

2 Making up Fold each of the sixteen fabric tab pieces in half lengthways and seam down their longest edge. Turn to right sides and press the seam, centring it down the back. Then with right sides out, fold each tab in half widthways and tack the raw edges together. Pin and tack four tabs at regular intervals along each side of the cushion cover ensuring that the raw edges match.

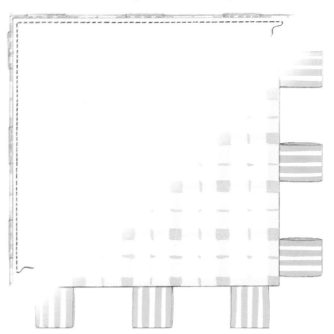

3 Finishing off Cut across the back panel, parallel with the short sides and seam and insert zip *see step 5 on page 11*. Place the front and back cover pieces, right sides together and tack and stitch all round the edge. Keep the tabs square as you work. Turn to right sides and insert cushion pad.

◀ *Check it out*
Here you can see a highly effective combination of stripes and checks in shades of blue and ecru. The use of a firm cotton, makes for a cushion cover, which is durable and easy to handle, when making up. Having made one cushion, you could reverse the fabrics to make a similar cushion with striped cover and checked tabs. Others could be made using a plain dyed cotton in matching blue or ecru.

Quick covers for plain chairs

Plain wooden chairs, somewhat battered but far too practical to dispose of, are to be found in all but the smartest houses. No matter how worn, these chairs always have a certain rustic charm, and often all that's needed to give them a lift is a splash of colourful fabric. The quick covers featured here will brighten up the plainest of chairs, and add a touch of comfort.

▼ Fabric inspiration
The striped borders and fresh floral panel of this vibrantly coloured fabric really enhance the design of this simple chair.

MAKING THE COVERS

Materials

Plain wooden kitchen or **dining chair**

Hardwearing furnishing fabric for the chair covers; use two different fabrics for the chair back if you want to make a reversible cover; (see instructions for quantities)

Mediumweight wadding to pad the chair back cover

Iron-on interfacing to stiffen the leg panels, if required

Matching sewing threads

Tape measure

This set of covers consists of a padded chair back cover, which will cushion your back against hard wooden cross rails, and a matching skirt made up of four fabric panels. Fabric ties hold the chair back cover in place, while the skirt panels are held on the chair by strips of fabric looped over the top of the legs. The skirt can easily be adapted to suit chairs whose legs start just below the chair seat, by using fabric ties, rather than loops, to tie it round the top of the chair legs.

▼ *Colourful transformation*
If your wooden chair has seen better days, smarten it up with a lick of paint. Strong colours, like this lively blue which has been sponged over a paler background look stunning and will give your fabric a real lift.

1 Measuring up For the chair back cover, measure the width of the chair back (**a**) from just inside the frame. Decide how far down the chair back you would like the cover to extend, then measure from this point on the front of the chair back, over the top and down to the same point on the back (**b**). For each skirt panel, measure across the respective edges of the seat (**c, d and e**) from just inside each chair leg. Then decide how far down the chair you would like the skirt panels to hang (**f**) – generally 11-15cm (4¼-6in), depending on the height of the chair.

2 Cutting out the chair back cover Cut out two fabric rectangles to the measurements taken, adding 1.5cm (⅝in) all round for seam allowances; make sure the fabric pattern is attractively positioned on the rectangles. Either cut both pieces from your main fabric, or make a reversible cover by cutting one from a different fabric; alternatively, economize by cutting one rectangle from a cheaper fabric with similar care qualities. Also cut a piece of wadding to this size.

3 Cutting out the skirt panels Cut out one fabric piece for each panel, adding 3cm (1¼in) to the width and 3.5cm (1 ⅜in) to the drop for seam and hem allowances. If using quite a lightweight fabric, apply iron-on interfacing to each skirt panel.

4 Making the chair back ties From your main fabric, cut four strips 22 x 6cm (9 x 2¼in). With right sides facing, fold each strip in half lengthways and stitch across one short end and along the long raw edges, taking a 1cm (⅜in) seam allowance. Turn strips through to right side and press flat.

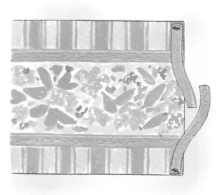

5 Tacking the ties in place Lay out one of the fabric pieces for the chairback, with right side up. Place one fabric strip at each corner, with its unstitched short end lined up with the long side edge of the fabric rectangle as shown. Tack in place.

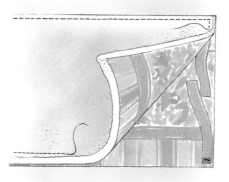

6 Stitching the cover Lay the second fabric piece over the first, with right sides facing and edges matching, and place the wadding on top. Taking a 1.5cm (⅝in) seam allowance, pin, tack and stitch around the edges of the fabric and wadding, enclosing the fabric ties as you go; leave an unstitched opening in one short edge for turning through. Remove the tacking stitches, trim the seam allowances, and turn through to right side. Slipstitch the opening closed. Place the cover over the chair back and tie it in place.

7 **Hemming the skirt panels** Turn 5mm (¼in) then 1cm (⅜in) to the wrong side along the bottom edge and two side edges of each skirt panel. Pin and machine stitch in place, mitring the corners. Zigzag stitch across top edge of panels.

8 **Stitching the fabric loops** For the skirt loops, cut four strips of fabric 20 x 6cm (8 x 2¼in). Fold and stitch the four fabric strips as for the chair back ties, but stitch along the long edge only. Turn through to the right side and zigzag stitch across one short end of each strip to neaten. Lay out the skirt panels, with right side up. Place a fabric strip on the right-hand side of each panel as shown, with the neatened end 1cm (⅜in) from the panel's top edge. Stitch the strips in place 2cm (¾in) from top edge of panel.

A secure finish
If you find that the skirt panels sag slightly, use Sew 'n' Stick Velcro to hold the panels firmly in place around the edges of the seat.

▲ Country freshness
Quick chair covers look most at home in a simply furnished country kitchen or informal dining area. Use them to decorate a set of chairs, or to brighten up a single chair that sits in the corner of the room.

9 **Hanging the panels in place** Fold 2cm (¾in) to wrong side along top edge of each panel, and pin the loose end of each strip in place on its neighbouring panel. Hang panels on chair to check fit, and make adjustments to length of loops until all the panels hang straight.

10 **Stitching the top edge** Remove the panels, mark then unpin the strips, and trim ends if necessary. Neaten with zigzag stitch and stitch in place as before. To finish, fold back the neatened 2cm (¾in) hem along the top edge of each panel and stitch in place.

15

FRILLED CHAIR BACK COVER

This pretty, slip-on chair back cover is ideal for chairs with a rounded back, and looks charming with a matching frilled cushion. A traditional gingham fabric suits the design, as do floral patterns.

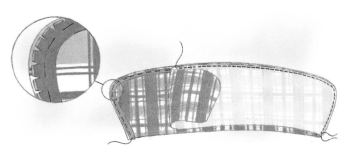

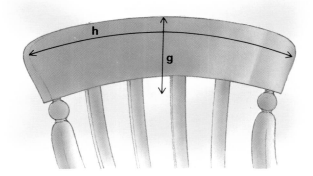

1 **Measuring up** Decide how far down the chair back you want the cover to extend (g) not including the frill. Then measure across this part of the chair back at the widest point (h), following the curve of the chair back where necessary. Add 10cm (4in) to each measurement for fitting plus hem and seam allowances.

2 **Making a pattern** Cut out two pieces of brown wrapping paper to fit your measurements. Hold the paper pieces in position at the top of the chair back, and carefully pin together along the top edge and sides. Bend and snip the paper for a good fit around curved corners. Use a pencil to trace all seamlines on to the paper pattern. Remove pins and take down the pattern pieces. Cut out the pattern pieces, allowing a 1.5cm (⅝in) seam allowance outside each marked seamline. Use the paper patterns to cut out two fabric pieces.

3 **Stitching the cover** Make up enough fabric-covered piping to run along the top and sides of the cover, and around the bottom edges. Taking a 1.5cm (⅝in) seam allowance, pin and tack piping to right side of back cover piece, around side and top edges; snip into piping seam allowances on curves. With right sides facing, lay front cover piece over back one and pin and tack together around top and side edges.

4 **Checking the fit** Slip cover over chair back to check fit, and adjust if necessary. Then stitch along tacked seams, trim seam allowances and turn right side out.

5 **Stitching the frill** Cut a strip of fabric 1½ times the cover's bottom edge by 8-10cm (3¼-4in) deep. Join the ends of the strip together to make a loop, then hem bottom edge. Run two gathering threads along top edge of strip and draw it up to fit bottom edge of cover.

6 **Attaching the frill** Taking a 1cm (⅜in) seam allowance, pin and tack piping to right side of cover, around bottom edge. Pin and tack frill in place over piping, right sides together and taking a 1cm (⅜in) seam allowance. Stitch in place then neaten raw edges.

▼ **Short cover** *This frilled cover is purely decorative, adding colour and a softer look to a plain chair. Try ringing the changes with different fabrics.*

Chair slips

Not everyone is lucky enough to own a perfect set of dining chairs. If yours are less than beautiful, with worn or faded upholstery, all is not lost; update them with a set of slip-over chair covers.

The smartest chair covers are short and neat in appearance, devoid of all fussy frills and trimmings. Simple skirts formed from straight pelmets are the most flattering for chairs with pretty legs. Add thin piping to the seams or chunky padded piping along the hems for a sharp contrast.

The addition of inverted pleats will highlight the shape of the seat, while splits inserted at each corner offer ease around awkward angles. Quilting the chair covers will add both style and comfort. Although not essential, the padding will also help to eliminate any fitting irregularities.

When choosing fabrics for your chair covers, take the opportunity to create a bold, new colour scheme. As the covers are easy to slip on and off, laundering is simple, so you can afford to choose fashionable fabrics with colours that don't need to be as practical as those suitable for upholstered covers. Bold red and white stripes are bright and cheery, while yellow and white chair covers create a sunny scene. However, for real impact, forest green combined with aquamarine creates a striking and fashionable colour scheme. It is very important to consider washing instructions when making your selection of materials and to ensure that the fabric is hardwearing and crease resistant.

The choice of cover styles will depend upon the shape of the chair. On pages 18–20 we show how to make covers for a kitchen chair, a spoon-back chair and a heart-shaped dining chair. Most of the designs feature a gusseted cover for the chair-back which is shaped to fit, and a neat little pelmet cover for the seat. Any of the designs can be adapted to suit other chairs; the set of covers shown on these pages can be made by adapting the instructions given and adding a flagged edge to the pelmet.

◄ **A ray of sunshine**
A sunny yellow fabric has been cut to fit this chair, creating a snug, removable cover. The flagged design echoes the pointed edges of the quilted tablecloth.

BUTTON-BACK COVER

Materials

Kitchen chair
Main fabric Firm-weave cotton furnishing fabric; see steps for quantity
Backing fabric See steps for quantity
Contrast-covered piping Size 6; see steps for quantity
Medium-weight wadding to add padding for the quilting; see steps for quantity
Contrast-covered buttons Seven for centre back opening and tab fastenings
Bias binding See steps for quantity
Tailor's chalk
Matching sewing thread
Newspaper, pencil and **ruler** for patterns

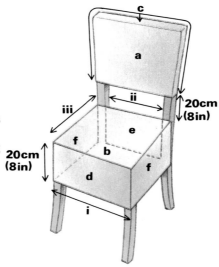

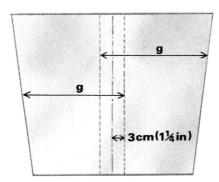

The back of a chair is quite often wider at the top than it is at the base. This makes it slightly more difficult to construct a slip-over cover if you want a snug fit. The solution is to make a fitted cover which will fasten at the back with buttons. However, the secret to obtaining a flawless made-to-measure finish to your covers, is to measure the chair carefully before cutting out your fabric. As an alternative, you could use an elasticated casing to fit the cover over the back of the chair.

1 Making patterns Place the newspaper over the chair-back and seat and mould it around the shapes. Remove and cut around the creased indents, trimming the length of the chair-back pattern by 20cm (8in). Check the fit on the chair and make any necessary adjustments. Mark the back pattern (**a**) and the seat (**b**).

Measure the perimeter and depth of the chair-back and, using these dimensions, draw and cut out the chair-back gusset (**c**). Also measure the seat widths (**i** and **ii**) and length (**iii**). Then, taking 20cm (8in) as a depth measurement, draw and cut out three patterns for the front (**d**), back (**e**) and side (**f**) pelmets.

2 Cutting out Pin patterns on the fabric with grains straight. Adding 1.5cm (⅝in) all round, cut one of (**a**, **b**, **c** and **d**) and two of (**e** and **f**) in main fabric, wadding and backing fabric. Now, using pattern (**f**), cut an extra two in main fabric. Then cut pattern (**a**) in half vertically to make the chair-back back pattern (**g**). Adding 1.5cm (⅝in) all round, plus 3cm (1¼in) to the width, cut four of (**g**) in main fabric and two in wadding and backing fabric. Next, cut two rectangles measuring 10 x 5cm (4 x 2in) for the tabs.

3 Quilting Sandwich each wadding piece between the wrong sides of corresponding main and backing fabrics, except the tabs. Pin and tack all round and up and down the fabric. Now machine stitch along the horizontal stripes. Repeat to quilt all fabric pieces.

4 Making the back cover Taking a 1.5cm (⅝in) seam allowance and with right sides facing, pin and machine stitch the unquilted and quilted fabric pieces (**g**) along the inner side edges. Press to right sides. Pin and machine stitch the gusset (**c**) and front fabric piece (**a**), right sides together, taking a 1.5cm (⅝in) seam allowance. Now pin and machine stitch the two back pieces (**g**) to the gusset with right sides facing, overlapping them along the upper edge to form the opening. Trim the seam allowance to 1cm (⅜in), snip off the corners and then bind the raw edges.

▼ Button chic
Smarten a jaded kitchen chair by making a set of covers, designed to echo the shape of the chair. The addition of padded quilting adds extra comfort.

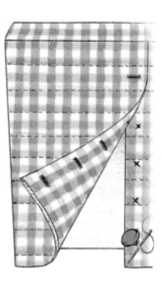

5 Adding fastenings Using the tailor's chalk, mark the positions of the buttonholes on to the centre back opening, ensuring they are positioned evenly apart. Place the first one 2.5cm (1in) up from the lower hem and ensure they are 3mm (⅛in) longer than the diameter of the button. Machine stitch the buttonholes in place. Now, mark the positions of the buttons on to the underside of the opening, and stitch a button over each mark.

6 Making the tabs Fold the small rectangles in half lengthways with right sides facing. Then, taking a 1.5cm (⅝in) seam allowance, pin and machine stitch together. Leave one short end open, trim the seam allowance to 1cm (⅜in) and snip the corner. Turn the tabs through to right sides and press along the seam. Using tailor's chalk, mark the position of a buttonhole 1cm (⅜in) from the neatened end of each tie. Now, machine stitch two buttonholes in place and slit open. Now, pin and tack the tabs into position, halfway down the sides of fabric pieces (**f**), with raw edges matching and right sides facing.

7 Making the seat cover Taking a 1.5cm (⅝in) seam allowance, pin and machine stitch the unquilted and quilted back pelmet fabrics (**e**), right sides facing, along the side edges. Repeat with the side pelmet pieces (**f**), machine stitching along the rear side edges and catching the ties in the seam. Press to quilted sides. Now, taking 1.5cm (⅝in) as a seam allowance, join pieces (**e**, **b**, **d** and **f**) together to form the seat cover. Trim all seams to 1cm (⅜in) and use bias binding to neaten raw edges.

8 Adding the piping Cut a length of fabric-covered piping 2cm (¾in) longer than (**e**) and pin along the lower edge, neatening ends by cutting piping cord to match the length of the back pelmet and turning the raw edges of the fabric under by 1cm (⅜in). Machine stitch in place, then turn a hem along the underside fabric and slipstitch the opening closed. Repeat to add piping along the lower front and side edges of the pelmet and also along the chair-back.

9 Finishing off Place the covers on to the chair and, using tailor's chalk, mark the position of the buttons on the back pelmet, to align with the buttonholes on the tabs. Sew a button over each mark and then fasten the buttons on both covers to complete.

SPOON-BACK CHAIR

Materials
Dining chair
Main fabric See steps for quantity
Contrast-covered piping See steps for quantity
Matching sewing thread
Bias binding See steps for quantity
Tailor's chalk
Paper, pencil and **ruler**

The gentle curve of this elegant spoon-back chair, is carefully imitated in the cut of the tie-on cover.

▶ **Flirty pleats**
Broad horizontal and vertical stripes give this gussetted slip-over cover a dramatic effect.

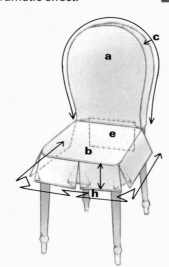

1 Making patterns Follow *Button-back cover, step 1* to make patterns (**a**, **b**, **c** and **e**). Now add the length of (**d**) to twice the length of (**f**), plus 24cm (9½in) for pleats, as a length measurement. Taking 18cm (7in) as a width, make pelmet pattern (**h**) for the chair-seat cover.

2 Cutting out Place patterns on main fabric, add 1.5cm (⅝in) all round, and cut one using patterns (**b**, **c**, **e** and **h**) and cut two using pattern (**a**). Now, cut twelve 20 x 5cm (8 x 2in) rectangles for the ties.

3 Making the back Cut piping to fit around piece (**a**) and machine stitch to right sides, 1.5cm (⅝in) from the edges. Place the gusset (**c**) and front (**a**) right sides facing, and machine stitch together over the piping stitches. Repeat for back (**a**), leaving 15cm (6in) vents at the sides. Snip and neaten with bias binding.

4 Adding ties Turn a 1.5cm (⅝in) hem to the lower edge and stitch in place. Fold ties in half lengthways, stitch the long and a short edge and turn to right sides; press. Stitch four ties to the gusset and back, at the top and base of the vents.

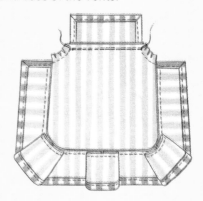

5 Making the seat Cut piping to fit around chair-seat (**b**) and pin then machine stitch in place, 1.5cm (⅝in) from the raw edge. Next turn a 6mm (¼in), then a 1cm (⅜in) hem to wrong sides all round the lower and side edges of pieces (**h** and **e**) and machine stitch in place. Taking a 1.5cm (⅝in) seam allowance, pin and machine stitch the pelmet to the piped chair-seat, right sides facing. Position three inverted pleats to the centre front and front corners. Now, add the back pelmet (**e**) to the seat (**b**) in the same way. Trim and snip the allowance to fit, then neaten with bias binding.

6 Finishing off Taking the remaining four ties, pin and machine stitch one to each corner at the rear of the chair-seat cover and then tie both covers on to the chair.

19

DINING CHAIR

Materials
Dining chair
Main fabric Firm-weave cotton
furnishing fabric; see steps for quantity
Contrast-covered piping size 1, see steps
for quantity
Matching sewing thread
Bias binding See steps for quantity
Tailor's chalk
Paper, pencil and **ruler** for patterns

This dining chair has a slimmer back
depth and therefore the cover for the
chair-back will not require a gusset.
Apart from this, the back cover is
made in exactly the same way as the
spoon-back chair, with the front and
back fabric pieces cut slightly larger
to accommodate the depth of the
chair back.

▶ Drama queen
*A beautiful mahogany dining chair is
given the regal treatment with the
boldest of red and white stripes. The
richly patterned damask cloth offers
a relief design, adding to the
formality. A slimmer chair back
affords a cover simply seamed with
cording, while the seat sits neatly
with the aid of the front vents.*

1 **Making the patterns** Follow
*instructions for Button-back chair
cover, Step 1*, to make patterns (**a, b,
d, e** and **f**) for the covers.

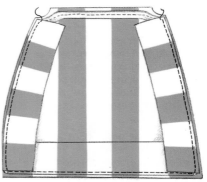

2 **Cutting out** Place all the pattern
pieces on to the main fabric,
ensuring that the fabric grains are
straight. Then, add 1.5cm (⅝in) all
round each pattern for seam
allowance, cut two in main fabric
using pattern (**d** and **e**), one using
pattern (**b**) and four using pattern (**f**).
Now, cut two using pattern (**a**),
adding 1.5cm (⅝in) for seam
allowance, adding the depth of the
chair back all round. Finally, cut
twelve rectangles measuring 20 x
5cm (8 x 2in) in main fabric for ties.

3 **Making the back cover** Follow
Spoon-back chair, Step 3 to make
the chair-back cover, ignoring the
gussets and adding a tuck to the
upper corners for fit. Continue, by
following *Step 4* to add the ties.

4 **Facing the pelmets** Pair up
pelmet pieces (**d, e** and **f**) with
right sides facing and, taking a 1.5cm
(⅝in) seam allowance, machine
stitch the side and lower edges. Trim
and snip raw edges and corners and
turn through to right sides. Press.

5 **Making the seat** Cut piping to fit
around the chair seat (**b**) and
machine stitch, 1.5cm (⅝in) from the
raw edge. Position pelmets, right
sides facing and raw edges matching,
on to the piped chair seat. Taking a
1.5cm (⅝in) seam allowance, pin
and machine stitch together. Trim
the seam allowance, snip the corners
and press the seam allowance
towards the centre. Now turn a
1.5cm (⅜in) hem to wrong sides
along the underside of the pelmets
and slipstitch the openings closed.

6 **Finishing off** Stitch a tie to the
four rear points of the seat cover.
Finally tie the covers on the chair.

Easy lampshades

Accessories such as lampshades are the final touch which complete the decorative scheme. Although there are many types of shade available, made from paper, fabric and synthetic materials, it's often difficult to find just the right one at the right price. Making your own to suit the room offers much more scope.

These designs all use a straight empire shade – a classic cone shape – as a base this suits a variety of decors and is readily available. Choose a lampshade style to suit the room, softly gathered or lacy for a bedroom, fitted and pleated for living and dining rooms. If you have never made a shade before these simple styles are ideal for a beginner.

▲ Gathers and frills
A fine fabric tightly gathered and stitched to the taped frame will still allow the light to filter through. A cream lawn has been used here but sprigged voile or a coloured fabric could also be used. Choose a pale peach, apricot or a soft yellow to create a warm glow.

21

Choosing a frame

Lampshade frames come in a wide range of shapes and sizes, but for beginners an empire shape is one of the easiest to work with. The frames can be plain metal or coated with white plastic. Plain metal frames should be painted with white enamel to prevent them rusting.

If possible, take the lamp base to the shop when choosing a frame so that you can check the proportions work well together. As a general guide the shade should be deep enough to cover the fitting, but not so deep that it obscures the base. Its width and shape should flatter the shape of the base.

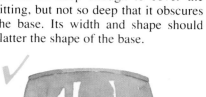

▼ The right proportions

The shade and base should be chosen with care – look at similar styles in the shops if you are unsure of the size of shade to match a particular base. The shade should cover the light fitting but not come so low that the size and shape of the base are lost.

too high

too low

too low

TAPING THE FRAME

The frame must be taped first if the shade is to be fixed to it. Using strong cotton tape (not bias binding) start by taping the struts and then tape the top and bottom ring. If you want the tape to match the shade, dye it with cotton fabric dye first. Measure each strut and round each ring and multiply by three to give the total length of tape needed.

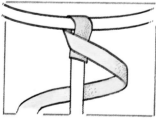

1 Starting to tape Cut a piece of tape three times the length of the strut. Starting at the top front of one strut, wind the end over the top ring, round behind and across to wrap over the loose end to secure.

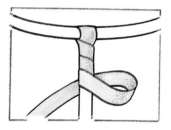

2 Taping the strut Work down the strut, wrapping the tape diagonally, so that each wrap of the tape just overlaps the previous one. Pull the tape very tightly as you wrap – once taping is complete it must not move on the strut.

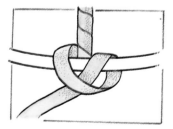

3 Fixing the end When you reach the bottom ring, pass the tape round the ring and back through the last loop to make a knot. Pull tight and leave the loose end of tape dangling for the time being. Tape each strut except one.

4 Taping the ring Measure the top ring, the bottom ring and the last untaped strut and cut a piece of tape three times this length. Wind up tape and secure it with an elastic band leaving about 20cm (8in) to work with. Start taping the top ring at the join with the untaped strut. Hold the end of the tape against the ring then wind it to the inside and back over the ring, catching the loose end under it. Work round the top ring as on the struts.

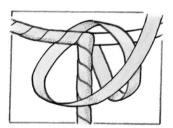

5 A figure of eight When you reach the join between each strut and top ring, wind the tape round the strut and ring in a figure of eight. When you arrive back at the untaped strut wind round this in a figure of eight and then tape down the strut. At the bottom of the strut, wind round it and the ring in a figure of eight and continue to tape the bottom ring in the same way as the top. When you reach each strut, trim off the surplus tape leaving 1cm (3/8in) and work a figure of eight over it to secure.

6 Finishing off Trim off any surplus tape to leave 6mm (1/4in). Turn under end and hand stitch to hold.

A frilled and gathered shade

A gathered shade should be made from fine fabrics such as silk, lawn or voile, which allow the light to show through the gathers. The top frill should be half the depth of the bottom frill. If you are using a very fine fabric the frills can be double with the gathering stitches running along the hem edges. Single fabric frills are preferable when using a slightly stiffer fabric, with a narrow double hem worked along the edge.

Materials

Straight empire frame taped as described on page 22.
Fine fabric, such as lawn or lining fabric
Sewing thread to match fabric

Single frilled frame

If you are using a slightly stiffer fabric, such as polyester cotton, a single frill is sufficient top and bottom. Cut the fabric the same length as below, but to calculate the width of the fabric required, add the depth of each frill plus 2cm (³/₄in) hem allowance for each frill. Stitch a 1cm (³/₈in) double hem along the top and bottom edge of each frill and run the gathering threads the width of the frill away from the edge. Continue from step 4 below.

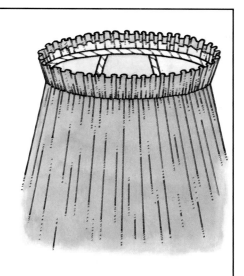

MAKING A FRILLED GATHERED SHADE

1 Calculate the fabric For the length of fabric required, measure round the lower ring and double this measurement on an empire shade, or add half as much again on a coolie shade. For the depth of fabric required, measure along one strut. Add double the depth of the bottom frill plus 1cm (³/₈in) hem allowance, plus double the depth of the upper frill plus 1cm (³/₈in) hem allowance. On the finished shade the hems of the frills will be level with the rings.

2 Stitching the side Join the fabric into a ring with a french seam.

3 Making the frills Turn up the frill depth plus hem allowance for a double frill top and bottom, turning under the hem allowance and machine stitching to hold.

▲ **Adding a frill** A bias strip has been used to neaten the top ring of this gathered shade with a gathered strip of fabric added to the lower ring for a frill.

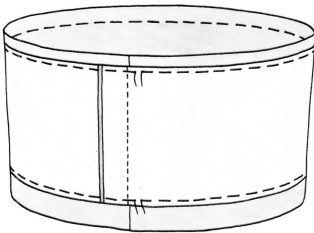

4 Gathering the frills Run a matching gathering thread the depth of the frill top and bottom. The rows of gathering stitches should be exactly the distance between the top and bottom ring, just above the hemmed edge. Starting with the top frill, pull up the threads to fit the top ring roughly.

5 Fitting the shade Place the shade over the taped frame, aligning the seam along one of the struts and pull up the threads to fit the top ring exactly. Fasten off and adjust the gathers evenly, pinning them to the ring. Pull up the gathering threads to fit the bottom ring, fasten off, adjust gathers and pin to frame.

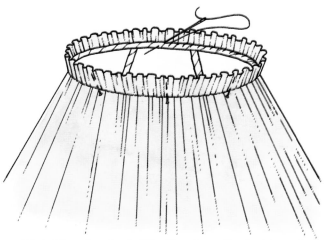

6 Stitching the shade Working from the inside, using small oversewing stitches, attach the gathers to the top and bottom rings.

MAKING A HANDKERCHIEF SHADE

This shade is quick to make as it is simply draped over an untaped frame. It is made from a circle of fabric which has been edged with lace and decorated with pearl beads which help to weight it slightly.

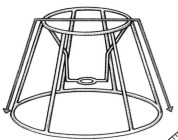 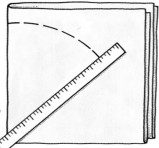

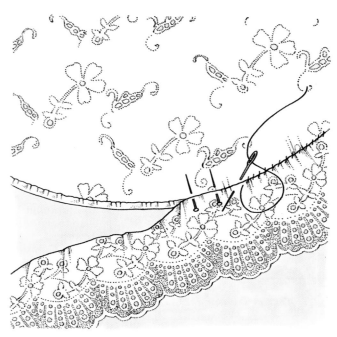

1 Measuring up To find the diameter of the circle of fabric needed, measure from the bottom ring, up one strut, across the top ring and down to the bottom ring again, adding about 10cm (4in) in total to allow for an overhang below the frame. Divide in half for the radius.

2 Cutting out Fold a square of fabric into four, with the centre of the square at one corner. Measure away from this corner the length of the radius, and mark the fabric at intervals, as shown. Cut along the marks, then unfold the circle.

3 Finishing the edge Turn a narrow hem to the right side round the edge of the fabric and stitch the lace over the hemmed edge. Turn under the end to join.

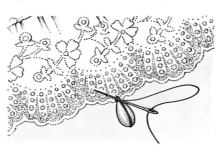

4 The final touch Add pearl drop beads spaced evenly around the edge of the lace and place the shade over the frame. Use a very low wattage bulb in the lamp to prevent the fabric from singeing.

◄ *A draped shade*
This pretty shade was made from a small square cotton embroidered tablecloth cut down to size and then trimmed with lace and beads. The broderie anglaise and the cutwork design looks particularly attractive with the light behind it.

Fabric wallhangings

Cloth has been used to decorate walls for centuries, fulfilling a multitude of practical and aesthetic functions. Whether you choose to drape every wall of a room with fabric hangings, or to simply decorate one or two with fabric panels, the result will be a softer, more luxurious interior than can be achieved with wallpaper alone.

As well as serving a decorative purpose, fabric wallcoverings will successsfully disguise badly finished walls and in addition add extra insulation and warmth. Individual fabric panels, like those here, make attractive cover-ups for areas of wallpaper that have become stained but most of all they are a great way to add colour to plain walls.

Your choice of fabric will depend on the type of wallcovering and the desired finished effect. The first question to consider is whether you would like the cloth to blend in with its surroundings, or to stand out as a real feature of the room.

If curtaining a whole wall it is generally best to opt for the subtle finish of the former. If only one or two individual panels are being introduced go for bolder fabrics.

▼ Set to match
Imagine this room without the fabric hanging and you can immediately appreciate its benefits. The wall takes on a three dimensional quality and makes the room seem cosier.

Hanging the fabric

There are several different ways in which to hang fabric wall drapes and panels; choose a technique which is stylish and practical. Slim curtain poles fixed high on the wall, provide excellent support for both drapes and panels. The fabric can be attached, using curtain rings, fabric tabs or ties, or sturdy clasps which grip the fabric and slide on to the pole.

Alternatively, lightweight fabric panels can be hung from a picture rail using picture hooks and wire. Another, more imaginative method for a fabric panel is to punch eyelet holes in each corner, and hang it taut across the wall with hooks.

Where the fabric is to be elegantly draped across the wall, metal rosettes or similar fixings can be used. These are attached in a straight line across the top of the wall, and the fabric is draped in graceful swags from one to the other. Where necessary reinforce the heading on fine fabric drapes with interfacing, so they can support the weight of the panels without tearing.

1 The best proportions Decide the size of the finished panel. To measure the drop of a tall panel, use a long piece of string tied to the curtain rod. Decide on the finished width of the panel's borders in relation to the central panel of fabric. Bear in mind that you want to display your chosen fabrics to the very best effect. Motifs on both fabrics should be kept centred and, if possible, whole. Experiment with different border widths to find a balanced and pleasing arrangement.

2 Cutting out the border From your border fabric, cut two strips the width of the finished border, by the overall length of the fabric panel, and add 3cm (1¼in) to each of these measurements for seam allowances. From the same fabric, cut a further two strips to the same width as above, by the overall panel width plus 3cm (1¼in). If possible, cut the strips so the fabric pattern will match well, across the corners when they are mitred together. Depending on the fabric design you may want the top and side border strips to be cut at right angles.

4 The central piece Cut a panel of your complementary fabric to the finished width and length of the border's inner measurement, plus 1.5cm (⅝in) seam allowance all round. Ensure the fabric pattern is attractively positioned before cutting out. With right sides facing, and side edges matching, pin, tack and stitch the border strip to the central panel taking a 1.5cm (⅝in) seam allowance. Press seams open.

A luxurious finish
For a sumptuous finish insert lightweight wadding between the fabric and lining. This will also improve the hang and body of fine fabrics.

MAKING A FABRIC PANEL

Materials
Two complementary furnishing fabrics one for the centre panel and one for the co-ordinating border
Lining fabric to back the fabric panel
Decorative trimming such as matching fringing, tassels or braiding to trim the lower edge of the panel
Brackets and **slim rod** from which to hang the panel; take into account the fabric you are using and make sure these are strong enough to bear the panel's weight
Matching sewing threads blue

The handsome wall hanging featured here is made up from two complementary fabrics and is finished with matching fringed braid. The panel is slotted on to a slim curtain rod, mounted on wall brackets. Fix the rod in place before you begin.

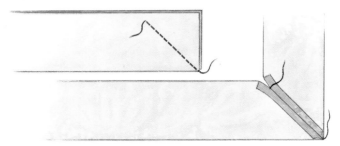

3 Making up the border With right sides facing, match two neighbouring border strips at one end and pin together. Fold in the corner at a 45° angle and firmly press the fold. Open out and tack along the fold. Remove the pins and open out the strips to make sure that the pattern matches then stitch the seam to within 1.5cm (⅝in) of the top edge. Trim off the corner, open out the strips and press open the seam allowances. Join together the other border strips, to make a frame.

5 Making up the panel Cut a piece of lining fabric to the same size as the finished fabric panel. With right sides facing and taking a 1.5cm (⅝in) seam allowance, pin, tack and stitch together around the top and side edges. Neaten the seam allowances and trim the corners. Turn the panel right side out, via the opening across the lower edge. Press.

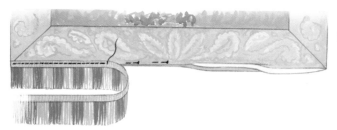

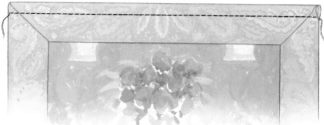

6 **Trimming the panel** Turn in and press a 1.5cm (⅝in) hem to the wrong side along lower fabric and lining edges of panel. Lay trimming along lower edge on right side, and topstitch in place, sealing turnings.

▼ *Eastern flair* Two striking fabrics from a co-ordinated range are combined to create this wall hanging. Both fabrics are printed with a distinctive design and an oriental vase completes the display.

7 **Forming the casing** Unpick the side seams at the top of your panel for 4cm (1½in), or more if you need a wider casing. Firmly secure any loose threads with knots. Pin, then tack and stitch across the panel through all layers, 4cm (1½in) below the top edge to form the casing. Carefully slide the finished panel on to the curtain rod and hang it in place on the brackets.

Designer wall drapes

Although wall drapes can be extended to cover a whole wall or room, they look most effective as individual hangings. The cheering news is that to create an individual wall hanging you only require one or two fabric widths. As well as being economical, they can be very simple to make. In its most basic form, the fabric wall hanging involves the very minimum of sewing and technical know-how; it can simply be hemmed and given a casing for the pole, then hung in place from the pole in no time at all.

Use wall hangings to disguise recessed storage areas or badly damaged plaster. As you have the choice to gather the fabric and hang it in deep pleats or keep it perfectly flat, the hanging can disguise a multitude of things, from uneven wall surfaces to an ugly alcove. Alternatively, use an extravagant fabric just as an ornament to make a design statement.

For a wonderful finishing touch you need to choose a stunning heading to hang up the drape. Either copy one of the designs shown here or experiment and create your own.

▲ Medieval dream

The wall hanging draped against the wall in this medieval-looking room is hung on a suitably themed metal curtain pole, complete with decorative finials. Although the hanging itself is one of the simplest to make, the addition of the imaginative flagged heading shows how you can transform a length of fabric into a stylish hanging.

To make this heading, place two wide fabric strips right sides facing and stitch together with a deep zig-zag seam to create the flagged points. Turn right sides out, and turning in the top straight edges stitch to the top of the main fabric hanging. Make a second parallel line of stitching across the heading to creating the casing for the pole.

◄ Alcove disguise

Two co-ordinating fabrics have been used to disguise a series of alcoves. The boldness of the fabric creates the illusion that each alcove is a door way, leading you from one room to another. In fact, these wall hangings would create a superb decorative option for a doorway.

Each wall hanging is finished with a slightly different lower edge. One has a simple border whilst the second features a padded hem. The flip over headings are made in a similar way to the flagged heading, above but tabs are inserted into the top seam.

Pelmet tablecloths

Dressing up a table is one of the quickest and easiest ways to transform a room. Old or ugly tables are best covered with a floor-length cloth; however, if you have a table with interesting legs, then top it with a short, fashionable pelmet cloth, which adds a flirty new look to the room.

Here, the slip-over tablecloths are decorated with interesting edges, and are perfect for a bedside or hall table. To create a dramatic impact, a length of turquoise silk has been made into an elegant, fitted tablecloth. Crystal drop beads are stitched to the points to emphasise the flagged pelmet. The

instructions for the pelmet can be adapted easily to include a scalloped edge like the one shown below.

▼ Impress your guests
Transform a small, folding table to match a particular room with a neat, fitted pelmet cloth.

29

FLAGGED PELMET TABLECLOTH

Materials

Main fabric Turquoise silk dupion, see steps for quantity
Lining White muslin to face the pelmet, see steps for quantity
Lightweight iron-on interfacing see steps for quantity
Self-covered piping in size 1, the circumference of the table, plus 3cm (1¼in) for joining
Bias binding colour-matched to the main fabric and 15mm (⅝in) wide, quantity the same as for piping
Crystal drops one for each point of the flagged pelmet
Matching sewing threads, paper and **pencil**

To accentuate the fit of the pelmet on this tablecloth, a dramatic flagged edge is added, with piping inserted in the seam for a crisp finish. By using a delicate coloured fabric, you can dress up a table for serving drinks on special occasions, or turn an ordinary dressing table into one fit for a star. Either way, the crystal drops add a brilliant finishing touch.

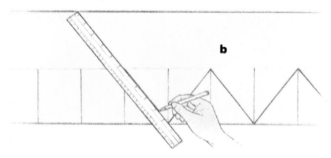

2 Drawing in the flags Lay pattern (**b**) out on to a flat surface and fold in half lengthways. Crease firmly along the fold and then open the pattern out. Divide the lower half of the pattern (excluding seam allowances) into an even number of spaces, each at least 10cm (4in) apart. Draw a flag between two dividing lines, as shown, beginning and ending the rectangle with a full flag.

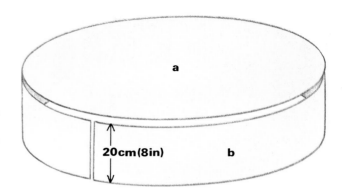

1 Drawing up the patterns Measure the diameter and the circumference of the table-top. Using the diameter measurement, draw up a circular pattern (**a**) for the table-top. Using the circumference as a length measurement and 20cm (8in) as the width, draw up a rectangular pattern (**b**) for the pelmet. You can make the pattern out of brown paper.

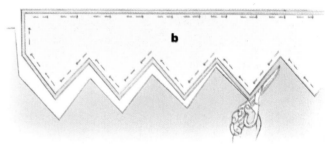

3 Cutting out the fabrics Position pattern (**a**) on to the main fabric, ensuring the fabric grains are straight. Add a 1.5cm (⅝in) seam allowance all round and cut one in main fabric. Then, using pattern (**b**), and adding a 1.5cm (⅝in) seam allowance all round (including the flagged edge), cut out in main fabric for the pelmet, one in muslin for the pelmet lining and one in interfacing.

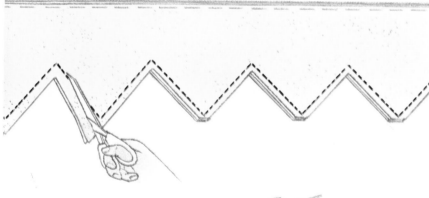

4 Adding the interfacing Place the pelmet interfacing and lining, wrong sides together and press to adhere. Pin the interfaced lining and pelmet main fabric with right sides facing and raw edges matching. Then, taking a 1.5cm (⅝in) seam allowance, tack and machine stitch together along the flagged edge. Trim the excess seam allowance to 1cm (⅜in), cut off the points and snip into the corners for fit. Turn the pelmet through to right sides and press along the seam.

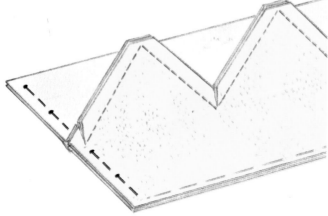

5 Joining the pelmet Take the two ends of the flagged pelmet and open out flat, so that the pointed edge stands up. Place the flattened ends together with right sides facing and raw edges matching, then, taking a 1.5cm (⅝in) seam allowance, pin and machine stitch together. Press the seam open, fold back along the pointed edge and tack the raw edges together, to close.

6 Adding the piping Pin the self-covered piping all round the right side of the circular table-top fabric, so that the raw edges match, then tack the piping securely in place. To check the fit on the table, place the circular fabric in position, so that the seam allowance fits over the table rim. Make any necessary adjustments, to the fit of the cloth at this stage, before making up.

▲ *All that glitters*
These lovely beads have a practical use; they act as weights to help the cloth hang.

7 Making up the cloth Place the flagged pelmet edge and the circular table-top fabric, so that their raw edges match and their right sides face. Then, pin, tack and machine stitch together, close to the piping, to create an even, neat seam. Now trim the excess seam allowance to 1cm (⅜in) and machine stitch the edges together. Finally, neaten the raw edges of the seam allowance using bias binding.

8 Finishing touches In order to add a touch of brilliance and to help the tablecloth hang well, simply sew a crystal drop bead to every point of the pelmet. Using tiny stitches, neatly oversew each bead to the fabric.

tip

Topping tables
To protect a polished surface on the table or the fabric top cloth, cover the table-top with a cut-to-fit sheet of glass. Available from most glaziers, the top should be made from toughened safety glass, with its edges bevelled and sanded smooth. You could also display photographs under the glass if kept out of the sun.

31

SCALLOP-EDGED TABLECLOTH

Materials

Main fabric in two co-ordinating bright prints. Ensure the fabrics will wash well together and see steps for quantities
Matching sewing threads of a suitable colour for both fabrics
Paper and **pencil** to draw up the paper pattern

A quick and inexpensive way of covering a table stylishly is a simple slip-over cloth. This one, edged with a gentle scallop, is very easy to make, taking no time at all. It looks great in any setting and the scalloped design combines beautifully with floral prints. Use two fabrics for a reversible option.

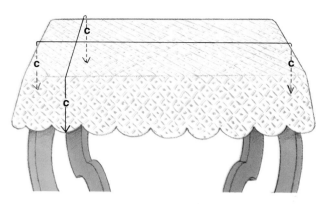

1 Measuring up the table Measure the length and width of the table-top and work out how deep you would like the cloth to extend over the edge of the table. Take your chosen extension and double it, adding the total to both the length and width measurements (**c**).

2 Cutting out Using these new dimensions, cut two rectangles in each of the co-ordinating fabrics, adding 1.5cm (⅝in) all round each for seam allowance.

3 Making up the cloth Place the two fabric rectangles with right sides facing and pin then tack together, taking a 1.5cm (⅝in) seam allowance. Then, draw in the scalloped edging with chalk.

Using these lines as a guide, machine stitch along the scalloped edge, leaving a sizeable opening in one side to turn through.

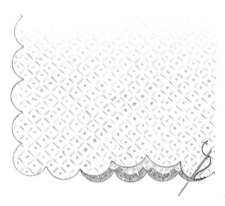

4 Finishing off Trim the excess fabric around the scallops, leaving a 1cm (⅜in) allowance. Snip into the allowance for fit, turn to right sides and press. Finally, neatly oversew the opening closed.

◄ **Harmonising blooms**
Choose two co-ordinating floral fabrics for a reversible slip-over cloth. Here, a range of pink blooms have been combined to create a pretty flowery-garden atmosphere on a bedside table.

Lined laundry baskets

A lining in your laundry basket will protect delicate items of clothing from snagging on loose bits of wicker, and is a pretty and practical way to brighten up a plain basket.

Any shape and style of basket can be successfully lined, whether cylindrical, rectangular or a curved Ali Baba basket. You can make either a purely functional lining that stops at the basket rim and is covered by the lid, or opt for a more decorative design in which the lining fabric is extended over the rim and is visible on the outside, as in the frilled version pictured here. Further splashes of colour can be added to the outside of the basket by decorating the lid, for example with a full fabric bow, or by binding the handle. It's always worth lining the lid of your basket as well – if the basket is full, your clothes are just as likely to catch on the lid as on the sides.

If your basket doesn't have a lid, use the lining as a cover-up for its contents. A drawstring top is ideal for a tall, cylindrical basket, while a flatter, wider basket can be covered with flaps of lining fabric which fall in from the basket sides.

The basket linings can be held in place in a number of ways. Gluing and stitching are two options, but if you want the lining to be easily removable for washing, use Velcro strips, elastic, or fabric ties, as featured here. Be sure to pre-shrink cotton fabrics, by washing them, before making up the lining.

Suitable fabrics
Firm, closely woven cottons or cotton mixes from dress and furnishing ranges are best for lining the baskets, and will stand up to frequent washing. Avoid flimsy or sheer fabrics which won't protect your washing or give good coverage of the basket. If you want to use a fine fabric, back it with lightweight wadding or interlining.

▼ Dressed to frill
Brighten up a plain laundry or linen basket with the addition of a colourful fabric lining. A prettily frilled edge or piped trim can be easily added and make charming decorative details.

Materials

Wicker laundry basket in size and shape of your choice

Lining fabric – see individual instructions for quantities

Binding in a toning colour to trim the baskets – see individual instructions for quantities

Fabric-covered piping for the cylindrical basket, made from the lining fabric; you will need enough to fit around the basket rim, plus a little extra for ease

Elastic for the cylindrical basket, a little shorter than the circumference of the basket rim

Lightweight wadding and **backing fabric** to quilt the lid of the rectangular basket

Sew 'n' Stick Velcro to fit around the rim and lid of the rectangular basket, for a removable lining (optional)

Tape measure

Matching sewing threads

Scissors

CYLINDRICAL BASKET

Tall, cylindrical laundry baskets are a popular choice, and can be lined in many different ways. Here, the frilled fabric lining is carried over the basket rim and secured around the outside with a concealed band of elastic. This lining is easily removed for washing.

1 Measuring up Measure the basket rim's circumference, and add 10cm (4in) for ease and a seam allowance, plus extra for pattern matching. Then measure the basket's depth, and add a further 30cm (12in) (equal to half the basket diameter plus turnings). Cut out fabric to this size for the lining. For frill, cut a length of fabric 11.5cm (4½in) deep and twice the basket rim's circumference.

2 Making the frill Stitch the binding to one long edge of the frill strip. Run two parallel rows of gathering stitches along the other long edge, 5mm (¼in) and 1.5cm (⅝in) in from the edge. Pull on the threads to draw up the strip to fit the width of your lining fabric.

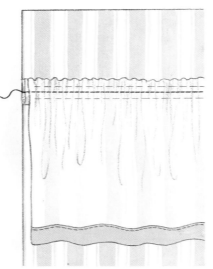

3 Attaching the frill and piping Lay out the lining fabric with right side up. Pin and tack the fabric-covered piping along the top of the main fabric, 5cm (2in) in from the top edge, which will be used to make a casing for the elastic. With right sides together, pin and tack the frill over the piping, taking a 1cm (⅜in) seam allowance on the piping and frill. Stitch the two to the main fabric, making sure you stitch close to the piping cord.

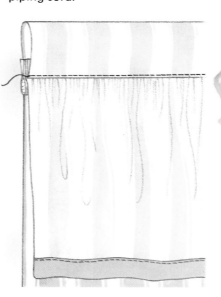

4 Making a casing Turn under 1cm (⅜in) of the lining fabric to the right side, along the top edge of the lining, then fold it over again so that its folded edge covers the frill and piping seam allowances. Topstitch in place to make the casing for the elastic.

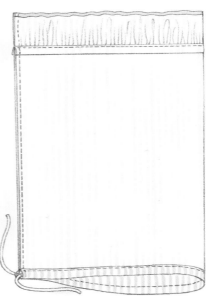

5 Making up the lining With right sides together, fold the fabric in half lengthways. Taking a 1.5cm (⅝in) seam allowance, stitch down the frill and the side of the lining to form a tube of fabric. Turn 5mm (¼in), then 1.5cm (⅝in) to the wrong side along the bottom edge of the fabric, and stitch in place to make another casing. Thread the casing with cord, then pull on the cord ends to draw the bottom end of the lining closed; tie cord ends into a secure bow. The cord can be released to make laundering easier.

6 **Inserting the elastic** Unpick a few stitches on the casing, on each side of the side seam, and thread through the length of elastic. Secure the elastic at each end and stitch the casing closed. Arrange the lining in the basket, so that the elastic holds it in place around the rim. Bind the lid handle with a strip of the lining fabric to finish.

tip

Decorative lids
Provided it matches your room, leftover pieces of lining fabric can be used to excellent effect to make decorative details for the lid of the basket. As your basket lining will nearly always remain covered by the lid, this is an ideal way to add splashes of colour to the outside of the basket. Use the fabric to make up a full bow or rosette, which can be easily stuck or stitched on to the lid; or simply bind the handle with fabric, for a simple but stylish finish.

▼ *Open and shut case*
Eye-catching details, like the quilted lid and contrast binding on this linen basket, make it look twice as stunning left open as closed.

RECTANGULAR BASKET

Rectangular wicker baskets can be used as linen baskets, as well as for laundry. Their shape makes them ideal for storing folded towels, table linen or bedlinen.

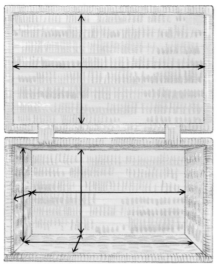

1 **Measuring up** Measure the width and depth of each panel on the inside of the basket, including the base and the lid; take the measurements from just below or inside the basket rim. Cut out one piece of lining fabric for each panel, adding 1.5cm (⅝in) all round. For the lid, also cut out a piece of wadding and backing fabric to the correct size.

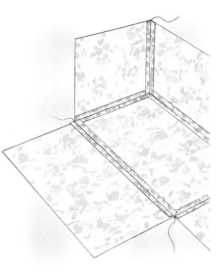

2 **Making up the lining** Stitch the lining panels together, taking 1.5cm (⅝in) seam allowances; begin by stitching each side panel to the base panel, then join the side panels together. Stitch contrast binding around the top of the lining.

3 **Quilting the lid** Sandwich the wadding between the backing fabric and the main lid lining fabric (right side up), and tack together. Quilt the lid in a basic trellis design, or use a more intricate pattern, if preferred. Trim the raw edges, then cover with contrast binding.

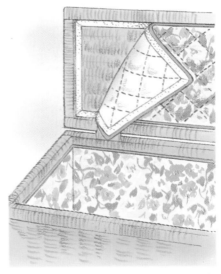

4 **Attaching the lining** This lining can either be stitched to the basket, or attached with Sew 'n' Stick Velcro for easy removal. To use the Velcro, slipstitch the stitching half to the back of the fabric lining, just underneath the binding, and also around the edges of the quilted lid. Then peel off the backing from the sticking half of the Velcro and press in place just under the rim of the basket on all inner sides, and around the lid. Press the lining in place in the basket and on the lid.

LINING WITH FABRIC TIES

This lining with its decorative fabric ties can only be attached to a basket with an open-work effect around the rim. The instructions given here are for a rectangular basket, but can easily be adapted for a cylindrical one.

1 Cutting out Measure the width and depth of the front, back and side panels on the inside of the basket, taking the measurements from just below the open-work rim; also measure the base. Cut out one piece of your lining fabric for each panel, adding 1.5cm (⅝in) all round.

2 Stitching the lining Join the panels together to make up the lining, as described for the rectangular basket. At the top edge of the lining, turn under 5mm (¼in), then 1cm (⅜in) to the wrong side to form a double hem; stitch in place.

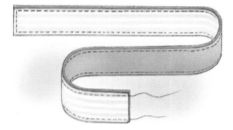

3 Making the ties The ties are made from the main fabric and a contrasting one. For each tie, cut one strip from both fabrics, 56cm (22in) long and 3cm (1¼in) wide. Place the two strips right sides together and, taking a 5mm (¼in) seam allowance, stitch together down both long sides and across one end. Turn through to right side and slipstitch other end closed. Press to lie flat.

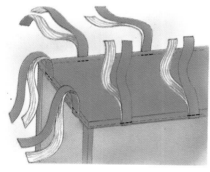

4 Attaching the ties Fold each tie in half width ways and pin in place along the top edge of the lining, to the wrong side; line up the folded edge of the tie with the bottom of the hem. Topstitch each tie to the lining. Tie the lining in place on the struts around the top of the basket, arranging the ties so that both the main and the contrast fabric are visible.

tip

Ways with wicker
To brighten up an old wicker basket which has seen better days, spray it with paint in a shade of your choice. Spray several light coats, allowing each to dry before applying the next, to avoid unsightly build-up. Braid, ribbon and knotted cord trimmings stuck around the base and rim of your basket will also look stylish, and add a touch of individuality.

▲▼ **Bow ties**
Tie the fabric ties in different ways to achieve a fun, haphazard effect, as shown here, or take a little more time for a neater, more regular look.

Simple fabric bedheads

If your bed head is a little old and worn, or clashes with a fresh colour scheme, you can quickly give it a new look with a tie-on or slip-on fabric cover. Simple headboard covers can be made in half the time needed to re-uphoster a padded headboard, and for a fraction of the cost of a new one.

The covers featured here can be used for all kinds of bed heads, whether padded or hard, like a wooden or even an iron headboard. If the headboard is hard, be sure to quilt the cover for comfort and a softer look. Tie-on covers are best reserved for rectangular bed heads, but slip-on covers can be made to accommodate the most unusual shapes and styles.

Washable furnishing fabrics are best for creating a hardwearing cover that is easy to clean. Choose a fabric which not only matches your bedlinen, but also

▲ Soothing stripes
Here, smart blue and white stripes, quilted along their length, bring a fresh new look and added comfort to a plain bed head.

blends well with the wallpaper and other bedroom furnishings – your bed head should provide a decorative link between the bed and the rest of the room.

37

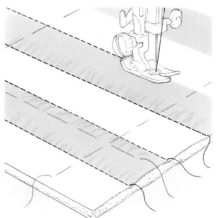

5 Quilting the cover
Quilting the cover Sandwich the wadding between the main and backing fabrics, with right sides out. Pin and tack the layers together at regular intervals. Machine quilt the cover in your chosen design: either take the fabric pattern as your quilting guide, as on the striped cover featured here, or simply use a basic quilting design, such as a trellis pattern. Remove the tacking stitches and trim the cover to match headboard measurements, adding 1.5cm (⅝in) all round.

6 Positioning the ties
Positioning the ties Lay out the quilted cover, with right side up. Position the fabric ties down both long edges of the cover, so they lie over the cover, with raw edges matching; pin one tie 3cm (1¼in) in from each corner, one just under a quarter of the way in from each corner, and the remaining four nearly halfway along each long edge. Fold the cover in half widthways to check that each tie on the cover's front lies directly over its counterpart on the back. Tack in place.

7 Attaching the side panels
Attaching the side panels Lay out the quilted cover, with right side up. With right sides facing, place the two hemmed side panels over the lower front corners of the cover; line up the raw side edge of each panel with the side edges of the cover, and place the hemmed bottom edge of the panel 1.5cm (⅝in) in from the cover's lower edge. Pin and tack in place, over the fabric ties.

Slip-on covers
If your slip-on cover rides up the bed head, you can hold it firmly in place with fabric ties. Simply sew pairs of ties to the bottom hem of the front and back panel, and tie them together under the bed head.

TIE-ON COVER

Materials
Rectangular headboard You can use either a padded or a hard headboard, as the cover is quilted

Furnishing fabric to cover the headboard (see steps 1 and 2 for quantities)

Mediumweight wadding and **backing fabric** for quilting the cover (see steps 1 and 2 for quantities)

Lining fabric the size of the finished cover, plus seam allowances

Matching sewing threads

Tape measure

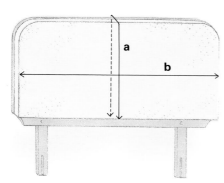

1 Measuring up
Measuring up Measure from the bottom edge on the front of the headboard, where it meets the mattress, over the top and down to the same point on the back **(a)**. Then measure the width **(b)**. Add 13cm (5in) to measurements for seams and 'shrinkage' during quilting.

▲ All tied up
Attaching the fabric bed head is easy; simply fold it over the existing headboard and tie at the sides. Side flaps conceal the original fabric beneath.

2 Cutting out
Cutting out Cut out one rectangle of your main fabric, together with one of backing fabric and one of wadding, to the required size. From your main fabric, cut another two pieces the full height of the headboard plus 4cm (1½in), by 18cm (7in) in width – these panels will cover the side edges of the headboard. Also cut 12 strips 23 x 7cm (9 x 2¾in) for the fabric ties. Cut out along the straight grain, and position the pattern on your main fabric so that it will lie attractively on the finished cover.

3 Hemming the side panels
Hemming the side panels Take the two pieces of fabric for the sides of the headboard. Turn under and stitch a double 1cm (⅜in) hem, down one long edge and across both short edges of these panels, mitring the corners for a neat finish.

4 Stitching the fabric ties
Stitching the fabric ties Take the fabric strips for the ties and fold each one in half lengthways, with right sides facing. On each tie, stitch along the long raw edge and across one short edge, taking a 1cm (⅜in) seam allowance. Turn through to right side and press flat.

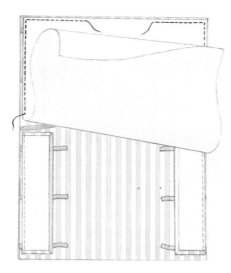

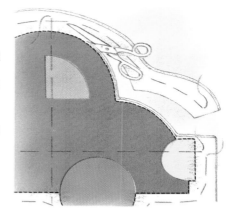

SLIP-ON COVER

Materials
Semi-circular headboard or **other shaped headboard** of your choice
Plain fabric for the cover (see steps 1 and 2 for quantities)
Fabric with large motif(s)
Mediumweight wadding and **backing fabric**
Fabric-covered piping

Padded, slip-on covers will suit any shape of headboard. Use bright and colourful motifs, or subtler images, depending on the desired effect.

8 Lining the cover Using the quilted cover as a pattern, cut out a piece of lining fabric to the same size. Lay the lining over the quilted cover, with right sides facing and edges matching. Taking a 1.5cm (⅝in) seam allowance, pin, tack and stitch the lining to the cover, enclosing the fabric ties and side panels as you go. Leave an unstitched opening along the lower back edge of the cover for turning through. Remove the tacking stitches, trim the seam allowances, and turn right side out. Slipstitch the opening closed.

9 Tying the cover in place Place the cover over the headboard. Carry the side flaps around the headboard sides and tuck them in under the back of the cover. Tie in place.

▼ A head for design
Any small child would love to have a bed like this. The large car motif matches the duvet fabric perfectly, while a smaller one has been used to trim the pillowcase.

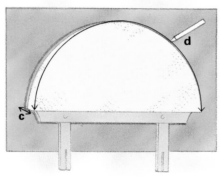

1 Making a pattern Lie the headboard over a large piece of paper, draw around outline and cut out to make pattern. For the gusset, measure the headboard's depth **(c)**, and distance from one lower corner to the other, measuring over top **(d)**.

2 Cutting out Use the pattern to cut out two pieces of main fabric, adding 1.5cm (⅝in) all round. Also cut a gusset strip to the measurements adding 3cm (1¼in) to width and 5cm (2in) to length.

3 Preparing the motifs Cut out your chosen motif(s), leaving a 5cm (2in) border all round. For each motif, cut a piece of wadding and backing fabric to same size. Sandwich the wadding between the two fabrics, right sides out, and pin and tack together around edges and across centre. Machine straight stitch around the motif, through all layers, following its outline. Trim to just outside the stitching line.

4 Stitching the motifs in place Lie the front fabric panel of the cover out flat, with right side up, and position the quilted motif(s) over it. Pin and tack the motif(s) in place, then check their position in relation to the bedding. Using a machine satin stitch, stitch around the outline of the motif(s), covering the raw fabric edges as you stitch. Also stitch in any details, like the window and wheels on the car motif shown here, using straight or satin stitch. Remove tacking stitches.

5 Attaching the piping With right sides facing and taking a 1.5cm (⅝in) seam allowance, pin and tack the fabric-covered piping around the side and top edges of both panels, snipping into allowance.

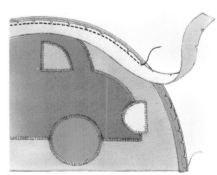

6 Stitching the cover With right sides facing and taking a 1.5cm (⅝in) seam allowance, pin, tack and stitch the gusset to each panel; snip into the gusset's seam allowances. Neaten seams. Along cover's bottom edge, turn 5mm (¼in) then 1cm (⅜in) to wrong side and stitch. Turn right side out.

39

Hanging bed heads

Hanging bed heads make stylish and practical alternatives to more traditional headboards, and allow just as much scope for creativity. One popular variation, shown below, involves hanging a wide panel of fabric behind the bed to form a striking backdrop. You can simply use the same fabric as for the curtains for a fully co-ordinated look, or introduce new colours and patterns into the room by opting for a different, though complementary, fabric.

CURTAIN BED HEAD

Materials

Fabric for the curtain – choose a fabric which will link the bed to other furnishings in the room (see step 2 for quantities)
Contrasting fabric to make the ties
Brass screw hooks and **wallplugs**
Matching sewing threads

1 Fixing the hooks Decide how far above the bed you would like the curtain to hang; to help you envisage the result, ask someone to hold the fabric up to the wall at your chosen height, then step back to check the effect. Insert the wallplugs and screw hooks into the wall at the required level, making sure they lie in a perfectly straight line, and spacing them 15-20cm (6-8in) apart. Position the first and last hooks slightly outside the side edges of your bed.

2 Preparing the curtain Measure the drop from the hooks to the floor (or to just below the mattress, if the curtain will be hidden at the sides of the bed), and add 4cm (1½in) for hem allowances. Cut and join fabric widths of the required length to make up a panel twice the width of your bed. Turn under and stitch a double 1cm (⅜in) hem down both side edges and along the bottom edge, mitring the corners.

3 Making the ties From your contrasting fabric, cut strips 42 x 8cm (16½ x 3¼in) – you will need one strip for each screw hook. Make up the ties as described in step 4 of the *Tie-on cover* (page 38), but stitch both short ends closed. Fold ties in half widthways, press, then open out.

4 Attaching the ties Lay the curtain out flat, with right side up. Pin, tack and stitch the ties in place across the top edge of the curtain, so that their pressed foldlines lie 2cm (¾in) in from the top edge and parallel with it; line the first and last ties up with the side edges of the curtain, and place the other ties at regular intervals across its width. Folding the ties up out of the way, turn under and stitch a double 1cm (⅜in) hem along curtain's top edge.

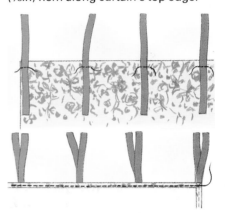

5 Hanging the curtain Hang the curtain in place by tying the fabric ties in full bows around the hooks, Arrange the bows so that they lie at the front of the curtain, where they will conceal the screw hooks behind. Dress the folds so that they lie evenly across the curtain.

◄ *Floral backdrop*
Although this bed head is easy to make, it always looks effective. Here a pretty floral curtain, with plain coloured ties, provides a backdrop for the bed, linking it to the other soft furnishings in the room.

Border ideas
Another idea for the curtain bed head is to use a fabric with a border, or a plain fabric with a contrasting border added along the curtain's top edge. You could use the bedlinen or the curtain material to make the border. To complete the look, add cushions covered in the border material.

Duvet bedcovers

Practical duvets have become today's most popular form of bedding, providing warmth and cosiness without the need for bulky layers of sheets and blankets. However, if you still find yourself hankering after the luxury and style of a floor-length bedcover, a smart compromise is available.

The 'duvet-bedspreads' featured here are essentially duvet covers extended to reach the floor with wide, sumptuously padded borders. These can be decorated with trimmings of your choice to create very striking designs.

The finished effect of the duvet-bedspread will depend largely on your choice of trimmings and the way you apply them. Appliquéd fabric strips in a simple, symmetrical design will look smart and sophisticated, especially if a classic fabric like a paisley or check is used. A feminine variation of this design is shown on page 43, where the appliquéd strips are given a soft outline by their frilled edging.

Alternatively, you can make use of the wide range of ready-made trimmings available, such as chunky twisted cord and tassels, ornate braid, broderie anglaise and lace, or whacky ric-rac braid in bright colours for a child's bedspread. Sketch out a few design ideas before you begin, to help you envisage the result. Use inexpensive, easycare sheeting fabric for the basic cover, and trimmings with the same fibre content.

▼ Gingham galore
Blue and white gingham is imaginatively trimmed with chunky cord or rope, to create a duvet-bedspread with a fresh, cottagy feel.

APPLIQUED BEDSPREAD

M aterials

Sheeting fabric to make up the bedspread and for the frilled border trimmings and piping. This is sold in widths of 230cm (90in); (see the steps for fabric quantities)

Contrasting patterned fabric for the appliquéd borders

Binding for the frilled trims; use a shade to match your main border fabric

Wadding and **backing fabric** for the padded borders (see steps for amounts)

Press fastener tape to seal the duvet cover; this can be bought on the roll

Piping cord to fit around the edges of the bedspread

Tape measure and **tailor's chalk**

Matching sewing threads

These instructions are for the smartly trimmed duvet-bedspread pictured opposite, and can be used for any size of bed. The appliquéd border design is easy to stitch in place, and looks very effective in natural coloured fabrics.

2 Cutting out Cut and seam together widths of sheeting fabric to make up a piece to the overall bedspread measurements (**a** x **b**); add 5cm (2in) all round for seams and ease, plus a little extra if you

1 Measuring up Remove the duvet and pillows from your bed. Measure from the floor on one side of the bed, up over it and down to the same point on the other side (**a**). Then measure from the floor at the foot of the bed, up over it to the bedhead (**b**). Measure the width and length of your duvet if you're not sure of its size. Standard duvet sizes are 200 x 140cm (79 x 55in) for a single, 200 x 200 cm (79 x 79in) for a double, and 230 x 220cm (90 x 86in) for a king-size. Also measure the width (**c**) and length (**d**) of your mattress.

want the bedcover to spread out on the floor. Try to position seams so they will lie under the appliquéd border strips (see step 7). Make up a second piece for the bedspread back, 15cm (6in) longer than the first.

3 Preparing the fasteners Lay the back of the bedspread out flat. Measure down from the top edge for the length of your duvet, minus 15cm (6in). Cut across the fabric in a straight line at this point. Along the cut edges, turn a double 2.5cm (1in) hem to the wrong side on the main fabric piece, and to the right side on the smaller piece. Topstitch in place. Cut a length of press fastener tape for the duvet opening; this should be 100cm (39in) long for a standard single duvet, 150cm (59in) long for a double, and 160cm (63in) long for a king-size.

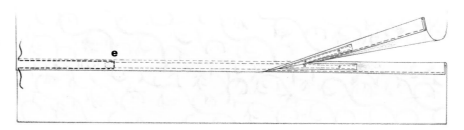

4 Stitching the duvet opening Pull apart the press fastenings to give two halves of tape. Stitch one half centrally along each hemmed edge of the bedspread back, on the side with turnings. Join the fasteners so

both fabric pieces lie right side up. Topstitch in from each side edge, over the turnings, to 1cm (⅜in) past the end of the tape (**e**). Then stitch straight down across the tape, and back out to the fabric edge.

5 The padded borders Deduct your duvet width from the overall width of the bedspread, including seam allowances and ease. Halve the answer to find the required depth of each side border, and add 1.5cm (⅝in) for an inside seam allowance. Cut two lengths of wadding and backing to this depth, by the overall bedspread length. To find the depth of the border at the foot of the bed, deduct the duvet length from the overall bedspread length, and add 1.5cm (⅝in). Cut wadding and backing to this depth, by the overall bedspread width.

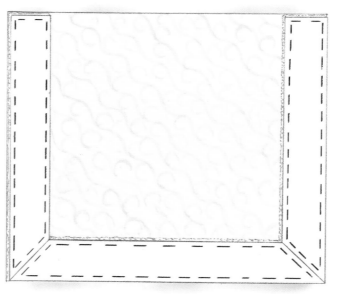

6 Attaching the wadding Lay the fabric piece for the top of the bedspread out flat, with wrong side up. With edges matching, place the strips of wadding then backing fabric on top, along the sides and lower edges. Where the wadding pieces meet, diagonally trim their ends and butt them together to form a neat mitre. If the padded border along the foot of the bed is wider than the side flanges, simply alter the angle at which you trim. Pin and tack the wadding and backing to the fabric, 1.5cm (⅝in) in from the edges all the way round.

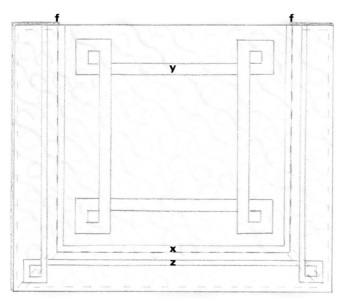

7 Marking the design
Depending on the size of your bedspread, decide how wide you want the appliquéd borders to be. Chalk the borders (**x**, **y** and **z**) on to the right side of your front bedspread piece, as shown. The middle border (**x**) should be marked up with its outer edge lying flush with the tacking lines along the wadding's inside edge (**f**); this border's edges will form the duvet casing. When marking up the inner border (**y**), refer to your mattress size (**c** x **d**) to make sure the design won't hang down over the sides of the bed.

8 The frilled trim
Measure along the inner border (**y**), and multiply by 1½. Cut and make up a strip of sheeting fabric to this length, by the desired finished frill width. Bind both the long edges. Fold the strip widthways into quarters and press the folds lightly. Open out, fold in half lengthways and press. Open out. Run a gathering thread along the long fold line, breaking at each widthways fold. Gather up each section to fit one-quarter of the inner border. Tack the strip in place on the front of the bedspread, making sure that the gathers are even.

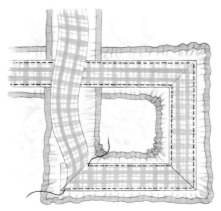

9 The border strips Cut and make up a strip from your patterned fabric, to the length of the inner border (**y**) by the required width; add 1cm (⅜in) all round for turnings. Press the turnings to the wrong side, and topstitch the strip in place centrally over the frill, mitring the corners. Remove the frill's tacking stitches. Measure up and cut out the other two patterned border strips (**x** and **z**). Stitch the outer one (**z**) in place as before, but stitching through the wadding and backing. Put the middle border (**x**) to one side.

10 Making up the bedspread
Make up sufficient self-piping to fit around the edges of the bedspread. With right sides facing and raw edges matching, pin and tack the piping around the edges of the front bedspread piece. Lay the back of the bedspread on top, with right sides facing, and stitch together taking a 1.5cm (⅝in) seam allowance. Trim down the wadding and turn right side out via the duvet opening. Press.

11 Stitching the casing
Lay the bedspread out perfectly flat, with the front face-up. Tack then topstitch the final border strip (**x**) in place as before, stitching through all layers to form a casing for the duvet. The raw edges of the wadding and backing fabric should be enclosed between the outer and inner lines of stitching. Remove the tacking stitches. Insert the duvet into the casing and match the press fasteners to seal.

◄ *Designer flair*
The appliquéd design on this duvet-bedspread lends it an air of sophistication and romance. For a less elaborate finish and quicker results, you can leave off the bound frill and only apply the patterned strips. (Instructions on how to make up the pillowcases with matching wadded borders are on page 44.)

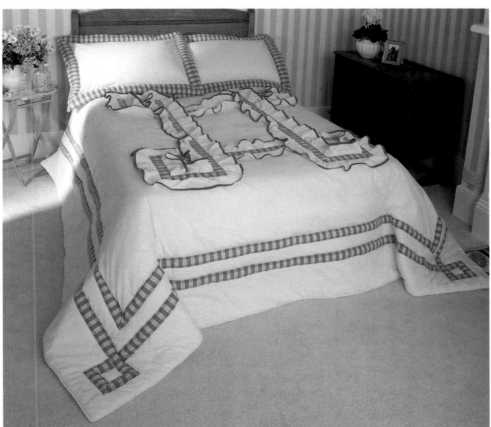

WADDED PILLOWCASES

Materials

Standard-size housewife pillowcase in a shade to match the bedspread

Patterned fabric for the wadded borders. You could use the main bedspread fabric

Mediumweight or **heavyweight wadding**, depending on how padded you would like the borders to be

Backing fabric

Matching sewing threads

Pillowcases with luxuriously padded borders look fabulous teamed with a duvet-bedspread, and really complete the look. The borders can simply be added to ready-made pillowcases, so you needn't spend time making them up yourself. Use the main or trimming fabric from your bedspread for the pillowcase borders, to create a matching set. The instructions given here are for a standard 75 x 50cm (29½ x 19¾in) pillowcase.

1 Cutting out From your main fabric, cut four 93 x 10.5cm (36¾ x 4¼in) strips and four 68 x 10.5cm (27 x 4¼in) strips for the pillowcase borders. Cut out along the straight grain, with the pattern attractively positioned. Repeat for the wadding and the backing fabric.

2 Stitching the border Join the fabric strips together to form two rectangular frames, mitring the corners as shown; stop stitching the mitres within 1.5cm (⅝in) of the inside edge. Repeat for the backing and wadding, diagonally trimming the wadding ends and butting them together into mitres. Oversew the wadding ends together, stopping 1.5cm (⅝in) in from inside edge.

▲ *Matching wadded pillowcases*

3 Attaching the border Lay the wadding then backing over one fabric border, on the wrong side. Tack together. With right sides facing, stitch the inside edge of this border to the front of the pillowcase, taking a 1.5cm (⅝in) seam allowance on the border, but just catching the pillowcase edge in the seam. Take care not to catch the pillowcase opening in the seam. Trim down the wadding and open out the border.

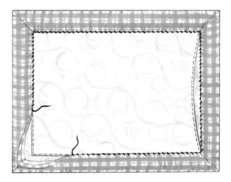

4 Finishing off Press under 1.5cm (⅝in) around the inner edges of the second fabric border. Stitch it to the wadded border around outer edges, with right sides facing. Hand stitch border's inner edge to pillowcase, machine stitching.

Dressing up a window

Windows provide the home decorator with virtually endless scope for creativity, and are well worth a little extra time and effort. An imaginative curtain arrangement, like this elegantly draped set will give a room character and flair, and create a striking focal point in your room.

The asymmetrical arrangement featured here consists of a luxuriously lined front curtain, drawn back to reveal swathes of delicately patterned lace. Both curtains are trimmed with a neatly pleated frill in co-ordinating fabric, and the front curtain is topped with an unusual 'puffball' heading, which softens the overall effect.

You can use this arrangement on almost any size of window, provided it is not too wide. The lace curtain makes an ideal cover-up for a plain window, as well as ensuring daytime privacy, and the treatment as a whole will create the illusion of a tall, grand window.

Use furnishing fabrics to make the main curtain and trimmings, selecting colours and patterns which blend with other furnishings in the room. As the arrangement is quite impressive and uses four different fabrics, make sure your choices are not so rich and colourful that they dominate the setting. The same fabric in different colourways often works well, creating an interesting, yet harmonious effect.

▶ **Perfect setting**
The luxurious softness of this window treatment makes it ideal for a bedroom, with the lace curtain providing essential daytime privacy, without blocking out too much light. At night, the main curtain can be let down to fully cover the window.

MAKING THE MAIN CURTAIN

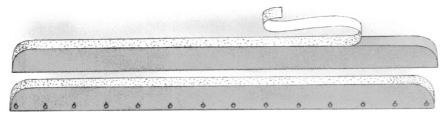

1 Preparing the batten Using a saw and file, shape the two front corners of the batten into smooth curves; use the edge of a saucer as your guide. Attach the sticky half of the Velcro to the batten's curved front edge, and staple it firmly in place. Then fix screw eyes along underside of batten, at back edge, spacing them about 7.5cm (3in) apart. Fix batten in place above window with the three brackets.

2 Measuring up Measure the drop from the batten's top edge to the floor, and add 7.5cm (3in) for seam allowances and draping. The width of the curtain is twice the batten's length, measuring along the curved edge. Join widths of your main curtain fabric to make up a piece to this size. Repeat with lining fabric.

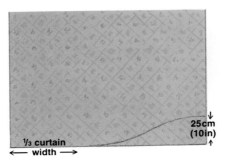

3 Shaping the lower edge Lay the main fabric out flat, right side up. Measure 25cm (10in) up from the bottom right-hand corner and mark a point with tailor's chalk. Measure roughly one-third of the way in from the bottom left-hand corner, and chalk a softly curved line from this point up to the first marked point, as shown. Trim along the marked line.

4 Shaping the lining Put the lining and main fabric together, with wrong sides facing and straight edges matching. Trim the lining to match the main curtain.

5 Cutting out the trimming Measure along the curtain's lower edge, and up the right-hand edge, then multiply this measurement by three. Cut and join strips of the frill fabric, 12cm (4 ¾in) deep, to make up a single strip to the required length. Fold the strip in half lengthways, with wrong sides facing.

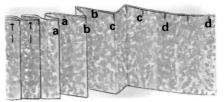

6 Pleating the trimming Choose a width for the pleats, eg 2cm (¾in). Use tailor's chalk to mark sections of this width along long raw edge of strip. Using the marks as a guide, fold and pin pleats in place (a to a, b to b, etc), with the pins at right angles to fabric edge. Stitch pleats in place, 1cm (⅜in) in from edge.

7 Attaching the piping and frill With right sides facing and raw edges matching, stitch the piping along the leading and lower edges of the main fabric, taking a 1cm (⅜in) seam allowance; ease the piping around the shaped corner, snipping into its seam allowance. Pin the frill over the piping, matching raw edges. Trim ends of frill to match curtain, turn in ends and slipstitch closed; at the curtain's top edge, finish frill 1.5cm (⅝in) from top edge.

8 Enclosing the weights Enclose each curtain weight in a little pocket of scrap lining, to prevent it rubbing against the fabric. Then stitch in place on wrong side of main fabric, placing one weight at the bottom of each seam, and one at bottom corners.

9 Attaching the lining Press 1cm (⅜in) to wrong side around lower and leading edges of the lining. With right sides facing, stitch the lining to the main fabric down the outer edge only. Then put fabrics wrong sides facing, and hand stitch together along lower and leading edges, enclosing raw edges and stitching into back of existing machine stitches.

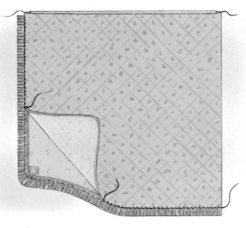

10 Preparing the heading Tack across the curtain top, 1.5cm (⅝in) in from top edge. Cut and join widths of frill fabric to make up a strip 35cm (14in) deep, by the curtain width plus 4cm (1½in). Stitch a double 1cm (⅜in) hem at each short end of strip. With wrong sides facing, fold strip in half lengthways and lay it across the curtain's top edge, with right sides together and raw edges matching. Stitch in place.

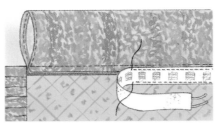

11 Attaching the heading tape Lay the top of the curtain out flat, lining side up. Press the seam allowances downwards and flip the heading up. Place the curtain heading tape over the seam allowances and stitch in place, enclosing all raw edges. Draw up the tape until the curtain is the required width; adjust the gathers to lie evenly, and neaten ends of tape. Hand stitch Velcro over tape.

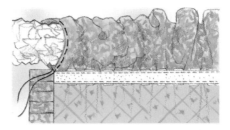

12 Dressing the heading Pull the folded heading strip open and run a gathering thread around each short end. Insert tissue paper into the heading, scrunching it down to

Materials

Two complementary furnishing fabrics – one for the front of the curtain and one for lining (see step 2 for quantities)

Co-ordinating fabric for the pleated trim and the puffball heading (see steps 5 and 10 for quantities)

Fabric-covered piping to match the lining; you will need enough to trim the lower edge and one side of the curtain

Narrow curtain heading tape to fit across the width of the curtain

Small, lead curtain weights

50 x 25mm (2 x 1in) wooden batten to fit the width of the window plus 20cm (8in); paint batten to match the window

Three 4cm (1½in) right angle brackets

Sew 'n' Stick Velcro the length of the wooden batten, plus 6cm (2¼in)

Brass or steel screw eyes

Small, clear plastic curtain rings about 12mm (½in) in diameter, for draping the main curtain

Fine blind cord

Brass acorn

Wall cleat

Staple gun and **staples**

Matching sewing threads

Tailor's chalk

Tape measure

achieve a soft, 'puffy' look, and allowing it to fall forward over the front of the curtain. Pull on and secure the gathering threads to close the heading. Hang the curtain on its wooden support by means of the Velcro and dress heading and folds.

13 **Draping the curtain** Use your left hand to draw the curtain over to the left side of the window. With the right hand, loosen the folds on the right of the curtain, to form a graceful curve along the leading edge, with increasingly gentle curves as you move across to the left. Ask someone to hold the curtain while you stand back and check the effect.

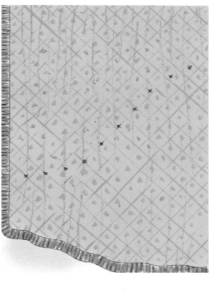

14 **Marking the folds** Keep holding the folds in place as you mark the back of each one with tailor's chalk, working across the lining in a straight line. Release the curtain – the marks should form a curved line across the curtain.

15 **Sewing on the rings** With the curtain still in place, sew small curtain rings on to the back, placing one over each chalk mark and stitching through both layers of fabric with tiny stitches. The first ring should lie 7.5-10cm (3-4in) in from the trimmed, leading edge.

▲ *Smartly pleated*
The crisp folds of a pleated trimming give a neater, more sophisticated finish than the flounces of a frill.

16 **Tying back the curtain** Fix the cleat in place on the wall to the left of the window, next to the uppermost curtain ring. Tie the blind cord securely to the front curtain ring, and thread it up through the other rings towards the back, untrimmed edge of the curtain. Thread the cord through the screw eye at the left end of the wooden batten, then trim it, so it remains long enough to allow the curtain to be released. Attach the acorn to the end of the cord. Draw back the curtain by means of the cord, and dress the folds, arranging the bottom edge so it drapes attractively to reveal the lining fabric.

Trimming ideas
For a fully co-ordinated look, you can apply the smart, pleated trimming on these curtains to a number of other soft furnishings in the room, such as cushions, tiebacks or a tablecloth.

MAKING THE LACE CURTAIN

1 Measuring up For the curtain length, measure the drop from the bottom edge of the batten to the floor, and add 3cm (1¼in) for seam allowances and draping. For the width, multiply the length of the batten by two, measuring along the straight edge.

2 Joining widths of lace To make up the curtain, join widths of lace using flat-felled seams. Place fabric widths right sides facing and edges matching. Pin and stitch together, taking a 1.5cm (⅝in) seam allowance and matching pattern. Trim one seam allowance down to 5mm (¼in), and fold other seam allowance over it. Open out the fabric, lay seam flat and topstitch in place, enclosing all raw edges. Make up the curtain so that its leading (left-hand) edge has the decorative finish.

3 Making the frill Multiply the curtain length by three, then cut and join 13cm (5in) wide strips of the trimming fabric, to make up a single strip to this length. Fold the strip in half lengthways, with right sides facing, and machine stitch along its length, taking a 1cm (⅜in) seam allowance. Turn the strip right side out and press flat, with the seam on the edge. Pleat up the strip as described in step 6 of *Making the main curtain*, stitching 1cm (⅜in) in from the folded edge, so that the seam lies on the outer edge of your trimming. When all the pleats are stitched in place, press them flat.

◄ **Lacy flair** *Trimming a lace curtain with a pretty fabric gives it a colourful and luxurious finish.*

Materials
Lace or net with decoratively finished side edges (see step 1 for quantities)
Decorative fabric for the trimmings and the tieback; use the same fabric as for the main curtain trimming and heading
Narrow curtain tape
Curtain hooks and **brass hook** to hold the tieback in place

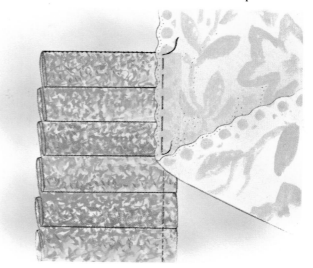

4 Attaching the frill Lay the lace curtain's decorative side edge over the frill, covering stitching. Topstitch in place, starting 2cm (¾in) from curtain's top edge. Turn in frill's raw edges and slipstitch closed.

5 Binding the raw edges Make up a strip of fabric the length and width of the curtain, by 12cm (4¾in). Press 1cm (⅜in) to wrong side along long edges of strip, and press in half lengthways, wrong sides facing. Enclose the raw back and hem edges in binding, mitring corner, and topstitch in place. Stop stitching 2cm (¾in) from top edge, and trim and neaten end of binding. Where the binding meets frill, neaten off and stitch together.

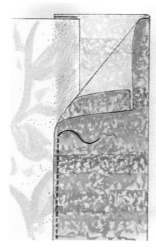

6 Stitching the heading Turn 2cm (¾in) of lace to the wrong side along the top edge, and place the curtain tape over it, enclosing raw edges. Stitch the tape in place and draw the curtain up to the required width. Use curtain hooks to hang the curtain on the screw eyes under the wooden batten.

7 Making the tieback Cut a 120 x 20cm (47 x 8in) strip of trimming fabric and fold it in half lengthways, right sides facing. Trim short ends diagonally into points. Stitch around the raw edges, leaving a gap in the middle of the long edge for turning through. Turn right side out and slipstitch opening closed. Attach hook to the right of the window, at dado level, and knot the tieback on to it. Use the tieback to pull back the curtain, arranging it into elegant swags, and secure with a bow.

Café curtains

The small, but engaging cafés of France, with their simple, fresh interiors, are the inspiration behind the use of half-length curtains in homes everywhere. At small kitchen or bathroom windows in particular, the artless, unaffected style of these delightful curtains is just right, helping to create a welcoming atmosphere and adding a dash of colour, without interfering with the clean lines of the room.

Café curtains are usually placed half way up the window, and are left drawn during the day. The top of the window is uncovered, so the curtains allow natural sunlight to stream into the room, while at the same time providing privacy from outside. If the window gets direct sunlight, the curtain can be combined with a long valance or with two short upper curtains which can be drawn back once the sun has moved round.

▲ *Twin trim*
A charming café curtain with a contrast tab heading, has been trimmed along the lower edge with the same fabric as the tabs for a very attractive, co-ordinated look.

Fabric choices

Any of the light or mediumweight fabrics suitable for standard curtains can be used for café curtains, although those with simple patterns usually look best. Since these curtains only have a short drop, you may need to watch the size of the pattern to ensure you get a reasonable number of pattern repeats – usually an odd number of repeats is most attractive.

For maximum light, the curtains can be made from lace, net, voile or other transparent fabrics, or from a lightweight fabric which largely uses a pale colour in its pattern. Since café curtains are usually left unlined anyway, most fabrics will let a certain amount of light through.

Crisp cotton or polyester cotton fabrics make lovely café curtains, but an intricate pattern may not show up well with the light shining through it. If the window gets full sun, and you wish to use a fabric with a complex pattern, you may want to add a lining.

The way the curtains look from the outside is another consideration. Some fabrics, such as checks or ginghams which have woven patterns, look just as good on the wrong side, but fabrics which have the pattern printed on, have a definite right and wrong side, so you may wish to give these a pretty lining.

MAKING A TAB HEADING

1 Cutting the main fabric Measure from the bottom of the pole to the sill, and cut out the main curtain fabric this measurement plus 5cm (2in). The width should be the width of the window plus 15cm (6in) for side seam allowances and ease. Cut out a facing for the top of the curtain 9cm (3½in) long and as wide as the curtain piece. Cut and apply iron-on interfacing to the facing.

2 Stitching side seams Turn under a double 1cm (⅜in) hem along each side edge of the curtain; pin. Slipstitch or machine stitch in place.

3 Cutting the tabs Decide on the finished width of the tabs – 5-7.5cm (2-3in) is average. With the right side of the curtain uppermost, and using tailor's chalk, mark the position of the first tab on each end, with one side close to the side hem. Mark the positions of further tabs spaced evenly in between – a gap of about twice the tab width works well. Count up the total number of tabs marked on the curtain, then cut out strips of fabric for each tab 23cm (9in) long by twice the required finished width plus 2cm (¾in).

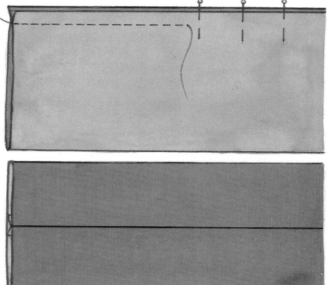

tip

Card trick

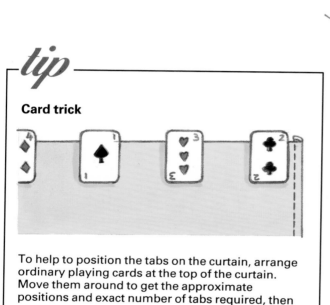

To help to position the tabs on the curtain, arrange ordinary playing cards at the top of the curtain. Move them around to get the approximate positions and exact number of tabs required, then use a tape measure to get the position more precisely. Since the curtain will be slightly gathered when in position, any slight variations in the tab positions won't show.

4 Stitching the tabs Fold each tab strip in half lengthways with right sides facing, and stitch the long raw edges together taking a 1cm (⅜in) seam allowance. Centre the seam on the tab, open out the allowances and press. Turn right side out.

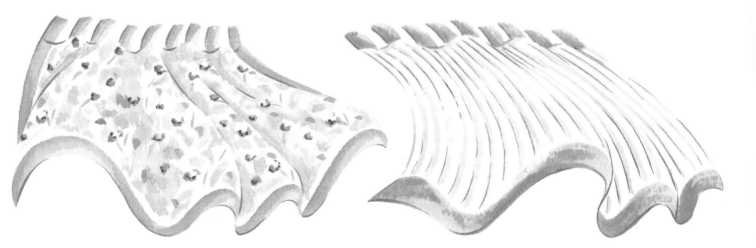

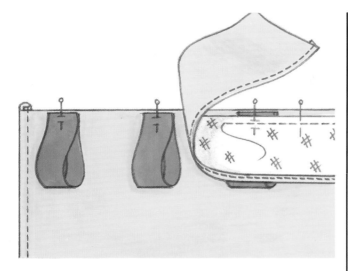

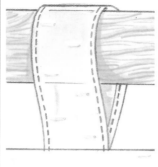

TAB VARIATIONS

Sheer fabrics When using sheers, the seams on the tabs may show when centred in the usual way. Instead, for each tab, cut a piece of fabric 23cm (9in) long by the width of the finished tab plus 4cm (1½in). Turn a double 1cm (⅜in) hem on each side edge, then fold in half, wrong sides together, and attach to the curtain as in step 5.

5 Attaching the tabs Fold the tabs in half widthways, with the seam inside, and pin in position on the curtain. Turn 1cm (⅜in) to the wrong side on the bottom edge of the facing and stitch, then place the facing centred on top of the curtain with right sides together and raw edges matching; tack through all layers. Stitch the seam, taking a 1.5cm (⅝in) seam allowance.

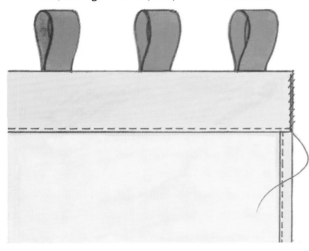

Lace Lacy fabrics with a finished lower edge make really lovely café curtains. For the tabs, buy a pretty, wide lace trimming with two finished edges. Cut into 23cm (9in) strips, fold right sides together and attach to the curtain as in step 5, left.

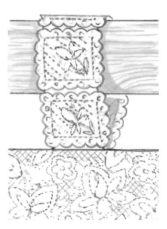

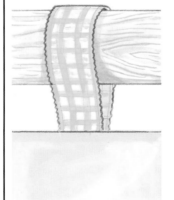

Ribbon tabs To make quick tabs, cut a length of wide ribbon 23cm (9in) long for each tab. Fold in half, wrong sides together and stitch to the curtain as in step 5 for a tab curtain, left.

6 Finishing off Flip the facing over to the wrong side of the curtain and pin so that the top seam is straight. Turn the sides of the facing under and stitch to the sides of the curtain. Position the curtain at the window and mark the hemline 1cm (⅜in) from the sill. Pin and stitch a double hem, then lightly press the curtain.

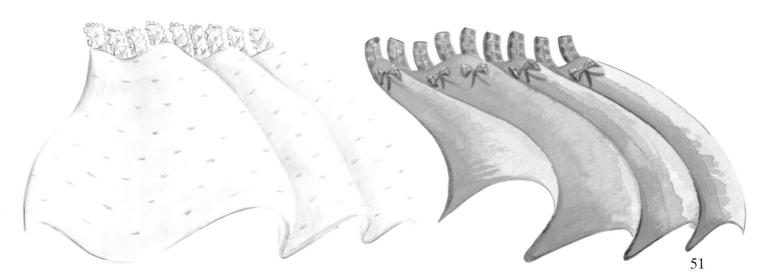

MAKING A SCALLOPED HEADING

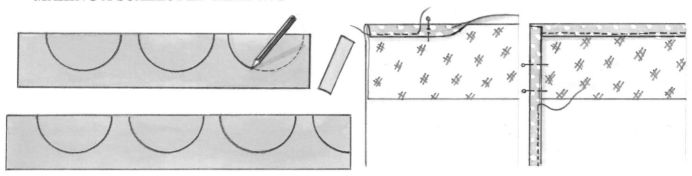

1 Making a pattern Cut out a strip of paper half the width of the window plus 10cm (4in) by 9cm (3½in). Cut out a semi-circle of card with a 10cm (4in) diameter and 5cm (2in) radius, using a saucer or compass for accuracy. With the card positioned 4cm (1½in) from the left end of the paper, draw round the card to make the scallops, following the diagram above. At the other end, trim the paper so that it finishes either 1cm (¾in) beyond a scallop or 5cm (2in) across one. Cut out the scallops, following the marked line.

2 Making the curtain Measure from the curtain pole to the sill and cut out the curtain fabric to this measurement plus 15cm (6in) long; the width should be twice the length of the paper pattern. Cut out a strip of iron-on interfacing 9cm (3½in) long and the width of the curtain piece. Iron the interfacing to the wrong side of the fabric, 1cm from the top edge. Turn 1cm (⅜in) of fabric to the wrong side on the top edge; pin and stitch. On the side edges turn a double 1cm (⅜in) hem to the wrong side; pin and stitch.

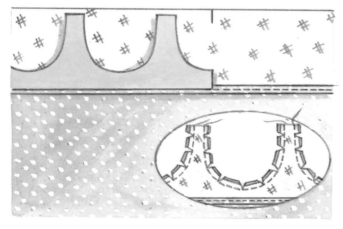

3 Stitching the scallops Fold the interfaced top piece to the right side; pin securely. Mark the centre of the curtain and position the paper pattern on top with the right hand end at the centre, and the top edge level with the fold. Draw round the scallops, then flip the pattern over and continue across the second half of the curtain. Remove the pattern and then stitch along the marked lines. Trim the seam allowances at the scallops to 1cm (⅜in) and snip to the stitching at intervals for ease. Turn right side out and press.

4 Finishing off Oversew the edges of the curtain and self-facing together, then stitch the lower edge of the facing to the curtain with hemstitch. Attach a curtain ring to the top of each scallop and thread the rings on to the curtain pole. Hem the curtain so it will rest 1cm (⅜in) above the sill.

London blinds

The London blind makes an ideal compromise for window settings where abundant frills of a festoon blind are over-elaborate, and the harder lines of a roller blind look too severe. This classic blind combines a simple tailored design with a gently ruched, scalloped base to create a look of elegant simplicity.

London blinds are best used on narrow windows so that the ruched scallop at the base of the blind is not so wide that it droops. To cover a wider window, simply make up two blinds and hang them side by side, or adapt the technique and make a wider blind by adding a third central tape to create two ruched scallops along the base.

In its simplest form, the blind is pulled up into soft folds by two side tapes, stitched to the back of the blind and, if preferred, disguised with decorative braid at the front. For a more formal look and a fuller ruched effect, inverted pleats can be added around the tapes as shown on page 54.

▲ **Simply stylish**
For narrow windows and where space is limited, blinds provide an excellent alternative to curtains which sometimes block out too much light. The classic London blind combines simplicity with elegance and can be adapted to suit all settings.

Fabric quantities

Where the blind is to sit inside the window recess, measure the width of the recess and add a 3cm (1¼in) side seam allowance. Then measure the height of the recess from ceiling to sill and allow an additional 13.5cm (5¼in) for the heading, plus 1.5cm (⅝in) for the bottom hem.

If you choose to hang the blind outside the recess, measure as above and allow an overlap of at least 3cm (1¼in) on both sides and at the top and base to prevent light showing through.

Materials

Soft furnishing fabric and **lining**
Austrian blind tape twice the length of the window recess height, plus 27cm (10¾in) heading allowance and 3cm (1¼in) hem allowance
Decorative ribbon or **braid** (optional) same length as Austrian blind tape but slightly wider, to match the blind fabric
Tailor's chalk
Wooden batten 5 x 2.5cm (2 x 1in), to fit the width of the window recess
Fine cord four times the height of the window recess and once its width
Two screw eyes
Staple gun and **staples** or use a **hammer** and 2cm (¾in) **tacks**
Cleat

▼ **Pleated elegance**
For a wide window, simply add a third pleat to the centre of the blind.

SIMPLE LONDON BLINDS

1 Attaching lining to fabric
Measure up and cut out the fabric and lining to the correct size (see fabric quantities). Matching the raw edges and with right sides together, pin and tack the lining to the fabric along sides and bottom edge, leaving the top open. Machine stitch the sides and bottom edge, taking a 1.5cm (⅝in) seam allowance. Trim the seams and turn the blind and lining through to the right side. Press, then pin and tack the two fabrics together along the top edge.

2 Marking position of tapes With lining side of the blind uppermost, use tailor's chalk to mark the position of the tapes, 30cm (11¾in) in from each side edge along the whole length of the blind.

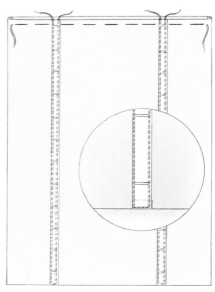

3 Attaching tapes to blind Cut the Austrian blind tape into two equal lengths, each of which must have a loop positioned 5cm (2in) in from the bottom end. Turn under 1.5cm (⅝in) at the lower end of the tape and place tape over the chalked lines on the blind, loop side up and with neatened end of tape at the base of the blind. Stitch down both sides of each tape and across the lower end.

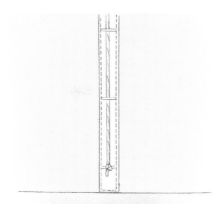

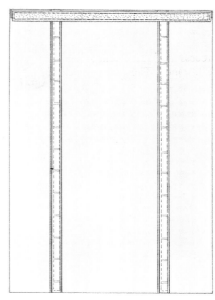

4 **Stitching braid to blind** (if required) Lay the blind out flat, right side up. Cut the decorative braid or ribbon into two equal lengths. Turn under one end of each piece by 1.5cm (⅝in) and position the braid directly over the stitches securing blind tape. Stitch down both sides of the braid along the whole length of the blind and across the lower edge.

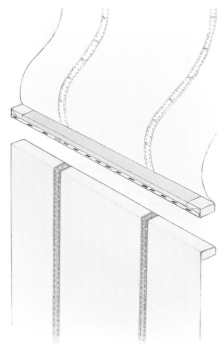

5 **Attaching blind to batten** Tightly cover both ends of the batten with scraps of the blind fabric, neatly gluing them into place and folding them round corners, as if wrapping a parcel. Fix the top edge of the blind along the batten with staples or tacks, wrong side to the batten, attaching it just under halfway up one of the narrow sides. Tightly roll the blind around the batten until all four sides of the batten are fully covered with fabric.

6 **Threading the pull cords** Attach the screw eyes to the underside of the batten directly above the two strips of blind tape, with the eyes facing the sides of the blind. Cut the cord into two pieces, one twice the length of the blind plus once its width, and the other twice the length of the blind only. With the blind lining side uppermost, tie one end of the longest cord to the lowest loop on the left-hand blind tape and thread it up through the loops to the top. Repeat with the shorter length of cord on the right-hand tape.

Thread the cords through the screw eyes above the tapes, slipping the longer cord through the second, right-hand screw eye as well, so that the two cords hang together at the side of the blind. Trim cord ends to the same length and tie together in a neat knot.

7 **Mounting the blind** Fix the batten to the ceiling of recess with fixing screws, so that the blind hangs level with the sill – make sure the blind is stretched tightly over the batten before mounting. Attach the cleat to the side of the recess to hold the cords.

VELCRO MOUNTINGS

London blinds can be attached to their support by means of a strip of Sew 'n' Stick Velcro, running along the top of the blind and across the front of the batten. This allows the blind to be detached and re-attached quickly and easily for washing and cleaning.

1 **Measuring up** Measure up as described previously, but add only 2cm (¾in) heading allowance rather than 27cm (10¾in), as the blind will not be wrapped around the batten.

2 **Preparing blind for mounting** Repeat steps 1 – 4 for making a simple blind. Once you have stitched the braid to the blind, place blind wrong side up and turn down the top edge for 2cm (¾in). Place the stitching half of the Velcro over the turned down fabric so that the top lines up with the folded top of the blind, and the bottom covers the raw edges of the turned down fabric. Trim ends of Velcro at both sides of the blind, then stitch in place.

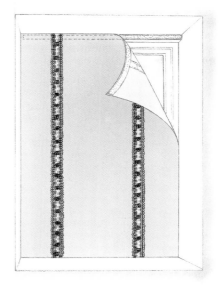

3 **Mounting blind** Paint the batten to match the window frame or cover it with same fabric as the blind, stapling or gluing fabric in place. Fix the batten to the ceiling of the recess. Peel off the backing from other half of Velcro and press Velcro along the top of the front of the batten. To secure the blind to the batten, line up two Velcro strips, then press together. Attach the screw eyes and add the pull cords as for making a simple blind.

PLEATED LONDON BLINDS

1 Measuring up Measure up the blind as for unpleated blinds, but add a further 34cm (13½in) to the width for each of the two inverted pleats, and add only 2cm (¾in) for the heading allowance as pleated blinds are attached with Velcro and not wrapped around the batten.

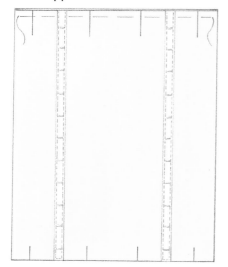

2 Marking the pleats Prepare the blind as described in steps 1-3 of making a simple blind. Once the tapes have been attached, do not attach any braid, but lay blind out with wrong side up and measure 17cm (6¾in) out from each side of the tapes at both the top and base of the blind. Mark measurements with tailor's chalk.

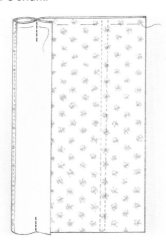

3 Stitching the pleats Turn one edge of the blind in, folding along the length of tape, and match up the chalk marks. Pin and stitch from the top edge of the blind towards the base for 9cm (3½in), and from the base towards the top for 6cm (2¼in) at the chalk marks. Repeat on the other side of the blind. Press the top and bottom of the blind with the stitching centred over the tape to form a pair of parallel pleats.

▲ **Choice of fabric**
Depending on the fabric used, a London blind can look equally effective in an elegant drawing room as in a bright modern kitchen. For the best results, use soft furnishing fabrics with an all-over pattern, like this fresh floral print.

4 Mounting the blind Because of the additional bulk of the pleats, pleated blinds are best mounted using Velcro, rather than by wrapping them around the batten. Follow the instructions in Velcro mountings on page 55.

tip

Fake London blinds
With a little trickery, the look of a London blind can be created in half the time. Hang a hemmed rectangle of your chosen fabric in the window recess and gather the bottom edge into softly ruched folds. Then simply stitch or pin the folds together at the height you want, securing them a little in from the sides of the blind so that they fall in a scallop across the centre of the window.

Use this fake technique as a temporary measure or as a refreshing change to curtains, or even as a permanent fixture on a window where you rarely alter the blind's height.

Sheer bliss

It is all too easy to resort to hanging plain net curtains at every window, just for the sake of privacy. But with a little imagination and using finely woven fabrics, like silk or lawn, really stunning blinds can be made. Both the blinds featured here, have been designed to take advantage of natural light shining through the window during the day. The white and lavender blind has been decorated with a tinted voile ribbon while the other blind featured overleaf incorporates a window panel decorated with cording.

Both of these blinds have been designed to be fixed to the window using a standard roller blind kit or if preferred they can be held in place by a fixed batten. The sheer fabric blinds are made in soft white silk or cotton which helps to filter the harsh rays, of sunlight, which can obscure vision and raise the temperature of a room, making the atmosphere uncomfortable. Both the blinds are therefore ideal for a conservatory or sun room.

▼ *Sheer delight*
Here, the white silk is decorated with a delicate lavender ribbon stitched in a twisting petal design, and makes a stunning blind for almost any window in the home.

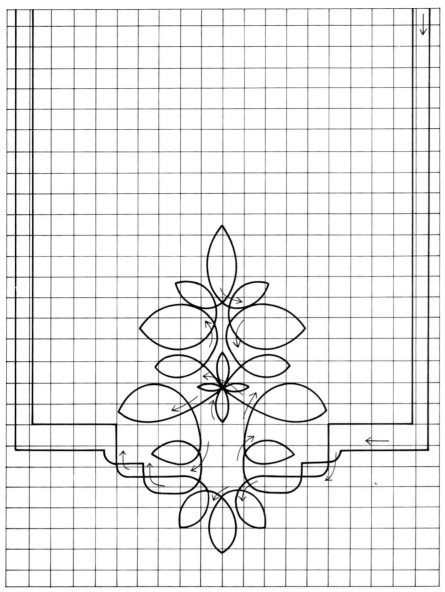

SILK RIBBON BLIND

Materials

Batten in a length to fit the width of the window

Main fabric ivory silk dupion or firm cotton, see step 1 for quantities

Offray sheer voile ribbon 16m (17 yds) in lilac, 1.2cm (½in) width

Matching thread

Metal retractable rule or **yardstick** to measure the window

Pencil and **tracing paper** (lightweight)

This striking silk and voile ribbon blind is very simple to make as the design is pre-planned and tacked on to the fabric as a guide. The ribbon is sewn on to the blind using one continuous length. Once the ribbon design is complete, and the casing is made the blind is ready to hang on to its batten. Alternatively, you can use a roller blind kit. Before you begin, fix the batten brackets in place on the window frame.

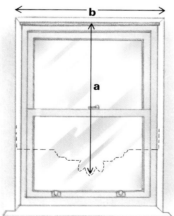

1 Cutting out Measure the desired drop for the blind from the top of the batten to the point where you want the blind to stop (**a**). Then measure the batten's length to give the width (**b**). Add 1cm (⅝in) to the width and lower edge for seam allowances, and an extra 7cm (2¾in) at top for casing. Cut a piece of fabric using these measurements.

2 Preparing the fabric Press and lay the blind fabric right side up. Turn a 5mm (¼in) wide hem, to the right side and tack in place. Stitch down the two side edges. The top and lower edges remain unfurnished at this stage. (The side edge hem will be covered later by the ribbon).

3 Transferring the designs Enlarge and draw up the pattern on to lightweight tracing paper. Pin the paper pattern on to the right side of the fabric, ensuring the lower decorative edge is straight and centrally placed. Mark the ribbon design on to the fabric, using white thread, tacking straight through the tracing paper and fabric. Separate the fabric from the paper pattern carefully, to avoid disturbing the design guides.

4 Starting the border Lay the prepared blind fabric right side up on a flat surface. Taking the reel of ribbon, unravel a length and folding the raw edge in, pin it to the top right-hand outer border.

5 Stitching the border Begin stitching the outside edge of the ribbon into place, following the design. Use the tacking as your guide and ensure that the ribbon covers the hem. It is important to keep the ribbon straight, but not taut and that your stitching is always close to the outer edge of the ribbon.

tip

Getting unstuck
The easiest way to handle such a long length of ribbon, the design uses one continuous 16m (17yds ⅝in) length, is to unravel a considerable length from the reel and wrap the excess around your neck, feeding the machine with ribbon gradually unwinding it from around your neck.

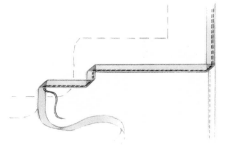

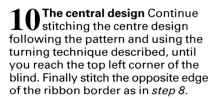

6 **Shaping the ribbon** When you have reached the lower edge, continue working the design, changing the direction of the ribbon, by folding and turning the ribbon at a right angle to face the left. With the needle in the downward position in the fabric, turn the blind to the right, so that the ribbon is once again facing you. Continue working the design, using this turning technique where the design dictates and keeping the stitches on the same side of the ribbon at all times.

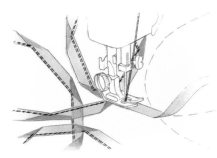

9 **The inner border** Return again to the top right-hand corner, take the reel of ribbon and unravel a second length. Pin the ribbon into place over the second tacked guideline at the top of the blind, enclosing the raw edge. This will form the inner border. Stitch the ribbon as before, following the outer edge.

10 **The central design** Continue stitching the centre design following the pattern and using the turning technique described, until you reach the top left corner of the blind. Finally stitch the opposite edge of the ribbon border as in *step 8*.

11 **Hemming the edge** With the ribbon design in place, trim back the fabric on the lower edge, leaving an allowance of 1.5cm (⅝in) and snip into the corners of the allowance to shape the edge of the hem. Turn the hem to wrong side and enclosing raw edges, slipstitch into place, hiding the stitches under the ribbon. Check the ribbon forms the edge on the right side.

12 **Finishing touches** Remove all the tacking stitches and then stitch the casing along the top edge thread the batten through the casing and fix on to the brackets.

7 **Shaping the edge** Having followed the tacked design, folding the ribbon into loops, you will finish opposite your starting point. Measuring the correct amount of ribbon to reach the top of the blind, cut 1cm (⅜in) extra and then fold the raw edge in and continue stitching to the top left-hand border.

8 **Securing the ribbon** Return to your starting point, repeat *steps 5-7*, but this time stitching the inner edge of the ribbon in place. Ensure that the ribbon remains flat against the blind at all times.

▶ *Twists and turns*
The ribbon is turned to create the curves of the petals and although just a series of folds and straight lines, the result is very soft and fluid.

BRAIDED PANEL BLIND

Materials

Batten to fit the width of the window
Main fabric white cotton lawn or similar firm cotton, see step 1 for quantities
Panel fabric white sheer gauze or firm cotton voile, see step 1 for quantities
Double stitched braid for signature
Matching thread, white
Metal retractable rule or **yardstick** to measure the window
Tracing paper (lightweight) and **pencil**
Steam iron and **spray starch**

Pure white cotton, starched and pressed until completely flat, forms a perfect border for the inset panel in this blind. The delicate braided rose signature and intended lack of colour, makes a calming combination. Before you begin, fix the batten brackets in place on the window frame.

1 **Cutting out** Measure your window as for *Ribbon blind step 1* (page 58) and cut the blind to these dimensions from the fabric, adding the required seam allowance and casing allowance. Enlarge the pattern given to suit your blind and place on to the fabric's right side. Ensure the inset panel is central and is a suitable height. Pin and tack in place, then cut a window from the main fabric using the pattern. Remove the pattern and use it to cut one piece from gauze adding 2cm (¾in) seam allowance all round.

2 **Preparing the fabric** Press the blind fabric using spray starch and a steam iron to create a stiff canvas. Turn a double 1cm (⅜in) hem to the wrong side on the lower and side edges. Then stitch a casing for the batten along the top edge.

3 **Applying the rose pattern** Trace the rose design from pattern (**a**) on to the gauze panel, using a white dressmaker's pen. Place the braid, on to the edge of the gauze and slipstitch in place by hand from the wrong side, around the outline of the design. Ensure the stitching is invisible from the right side and use a continuous length of braid.

Chart a

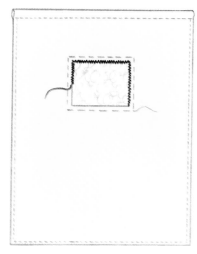

▲ Panel of light
A simple panel of white cotton lawn, is hung in a deep set window and is given interest with a lovely inset of braiding. The word 'rose' is signed over and over again, forming the pattern and disguising its message. If you wanted you could scribe other words but try and keep it simple.

4 **Adding the inset panel** Place the wrong side of the blind fabric on to the right side of the braided rose signature panel. Then pin and tack in place, making sure it is centrally placed. Using white thread and satin stitch, join the pieces together around the edge, neatening the panel frame at the same time.

5 **Finishing touches** Turn the blind fabric over and trim away the excess seam allowance, close to the satin stitches. Then, remove all the tacking stitches and thread the batten through the casing already in place on the top edge of the blind. Fix the batten to the brackets.

ISBN 978-1-4950-8819-3

7777 W. BLUEMOUND RD. P.O. BOX 13819 MILWAUKEE, WI 53213

Visit Hal Leonard Online at
www.halleonard.com

HAIR UP

Words and Music by JUSTIN TIMBERLAKE,
SHELLBACK, MAX MARTIN, SAVAN KOTECHA
and OSCAR HOLTER

CAN'T STOP THE FEELING

Words and Music by JUSTIN TIMBERLAKE,
MAX MARTIN and SHELLBACK

Moderate Funk groove

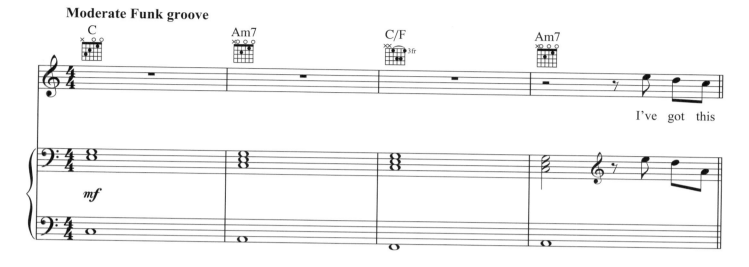

I've got this

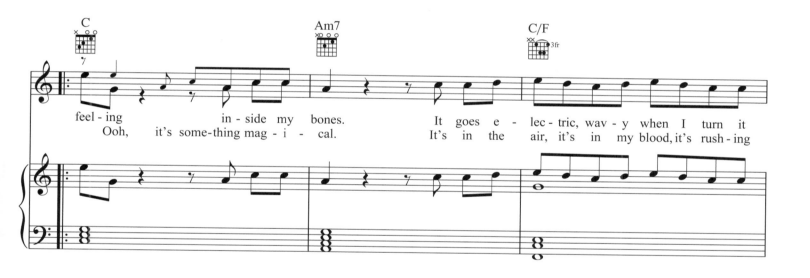

feel-ing   in-side my bones.   It goes e - lec-tric, wav - y when I turn it
Ooh,   it's some-thing mag - i - cal.   It's in the   air, it's in my blood, it's rush-ing

on.   All through my   cit - y,   all through my   home, ___   we're fly - ing
on.   I don't need no   rea - son,   don't need con - trol. ___   I fly so

I can't stop the...

I can't stop the,

N.C.

I can't stop the, I can't stop the feel - ing.
Noth-ing I ___ can see ___ but you ___ when you

I can't stop the feel - ing. _____
dance, dance, dance. I feel a good, ___ good creep - ing up ___ on you, ___ so just

I can't stop the feel - ing.
dance, dance, dance. Come on! All those things ___ I should - n't do, ___ but you

MOVE YOUR FEET/D.A.N.C.E/
IT'S A SUNSHINE DAY

"MOVE YOUR FEET"
Words and Music by
JESPER MORTENSEN

Moderate dance groove

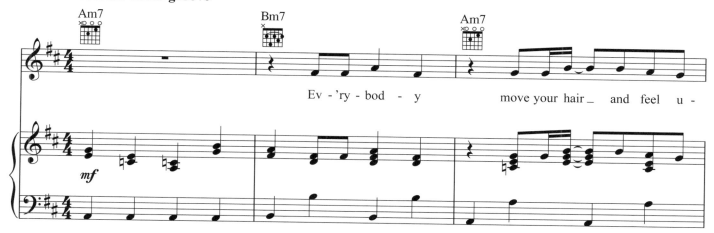

Ev -'ry-bod - y   move your hair __ and feel u -

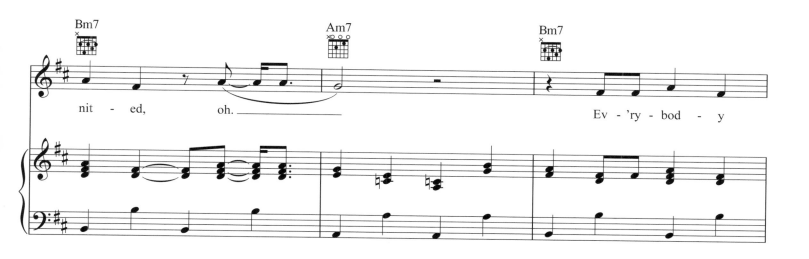

nit - ed,   oh. _____   Ev -'ry-bod - y

shake your hair __ and feel u - nit - ed,   oh. _____

22

"D.A.N.C.E."
Words and Music by JESSIE CHATON,
GASPARD AUGE and XAVIER DE ROSNAY

Additional Lyrics

Rap 1: Everybody's comin' to the celebration. I'mma hook you up with the invitation.
Let your hair swing and party with me. No bad vibes, just love. You'll see.

Rap 2: Aw, it ain't hard out here. when you're doin' it right. Put a smile on blast, that's the troll life.
And I'm here to help you through it. Come on Smidge, I know you can do it. Your confidence gives me strength.

GET BACK UP AGAIN

Words and Music by JUSTIN PAUL
and BENJ PASEK

I real-ly hope _ I can do it, 'cause they're all de-pend ing on me. I

know that I must leave the on-ly home I've ev-er known and brave the dan - gers of the for-est.

_ Sav-ing them _ be-fore they're eat - en. I mean,

THE SOUND OF SILENCE

Words and Music by
PAUL SIMON

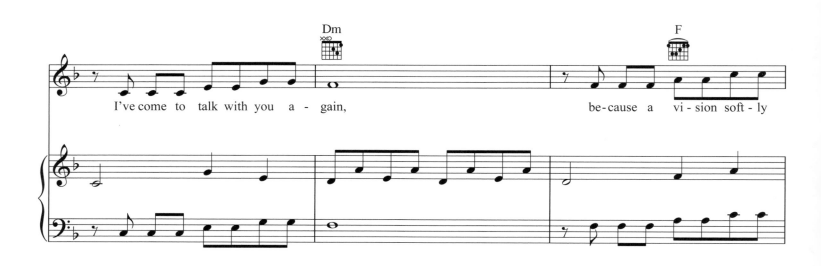

HELLO

Words and Music by
LIONEL RICHIE

Slow Ballad

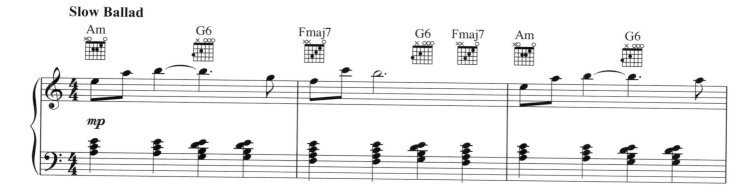

I've been a-lone with you in-side my _____ mind _____ and
long to see the sun-light in your _____ hair _____ and

Instrumental solo

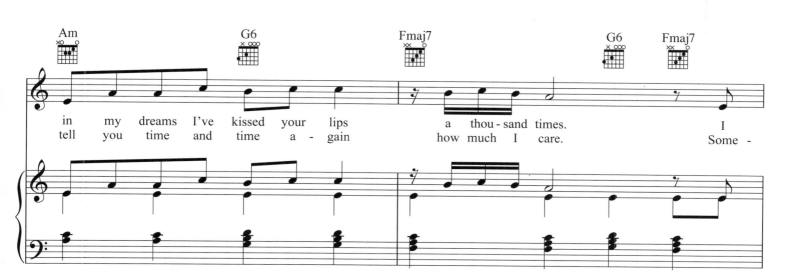

in my dreams I've kissed your lips a thou-sand times.   I
tell you time and time a-gain how much I care.   Some -

some-times see you pass out-side my door. ____ Hel - lo,   is it
times I feel my heart will o - ver - flow. ____ Hel - lo,   I've just
Solo ends   Hel - lo,   is it

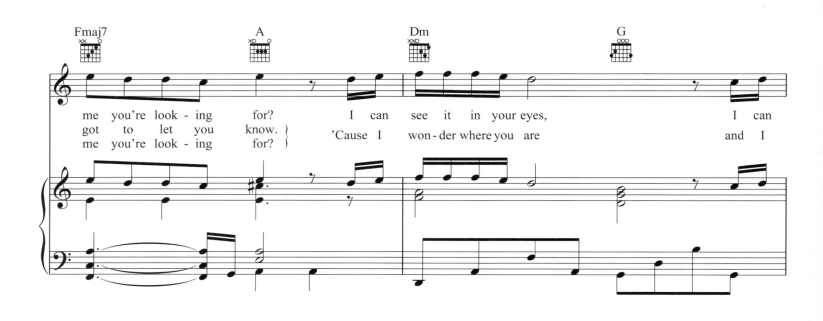

me you're look - ing for?   I can see it in your eyes,   I can
got to let you know.   'Cause I won-der where you are   and I
me you're look - ing for?

see it in your smile. ____ You're all I've ev - er want-ed ____ and my
won - der what you do. ____ Are you some - where feel - ing lone - ly ____ or is

I'M COMING OUT/
MO' MONEY MO' PROBLEMS

"I'M COMING OUT"
Words and Music by NILE RODGERS
and BERNARD EDWARDS

Slowly, freely

You, you, you, you, you, _____ you got-ta let it show. ____

Moderate groove

I'm com - in', ___ I'm com

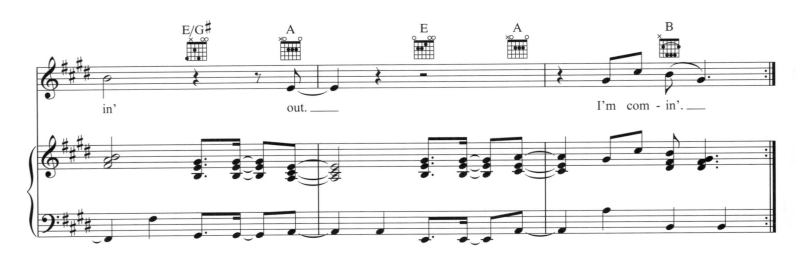

in' out. ____ I'm com - in'. ____

"MO' MONEY MO' PROBLEMS"

Words and Music by SEAN COMBS, CRISTOPHER WALLACE, MASON BETHA,
STEVEN JORDAN, NILE RODGERS and BERNARD EDWARDS

Rap: *(See additional lyrics.)*

She's com-in' out. (She's com-in'.) It's time to take a ___ stand ___

___ and show the world that ___ I'm ___ She's ___ com-in' out. ___
com - in' out. ___

Additional Lyrics

Rap: Yo! I'm comin' out like the sun after rain. Ready to shine, no time to be a flame.
Feelin' good, gonna get, get what I, what I want. Gonna show er', everybody hella, hella, c'mon.
Look at me now, my company it's s-soarin'. Dudes be impressed with the points I'm scorin'.
Like, "That ain't boring." And I just don't quit. Watch, you can't drop a show when I'm shakin' my hips. I'm sayin'...

THEY DON'T KNOW

Words and Music by JUSTIN TIMBERLAKE,
SAVAN KOTECHA and ILYA

Moderate Pop groove

TRUE COLORS

Words and Music by BILLY STEINBERG
and TOM KELLY

SEPTEMBER

Words and Music by MAURICE WHITE,
AL McKAY and ALLEE WILLIS

Additional Lyrics

3. My thoughts are with you,
   Holding hands with your heart,
   To see you, only blue talk and love.
   Remember how we knew love was here to stay?

4. Now December found the love that we shared,
   September, only blue talk and love.
   Remember the true love we share today.
   Chorus

WHAT U WORKIN' WITH?

Words and Music by JUSTIN TIMBERLAKE,
MAX MARTIN, SAVAN KOTECHA,
PETER SVENSSON and ILYA

EGMONT

The Best of 70s Girls' Comics Annual
First published in Great Britain 2014
By Egmont UK Limited
The Yellow Building, 1 Nicholas Road, London W11 4AN
All rights reserved

Please note: Some of the material used in this annual is exceedingly rare,
so the print quality may vary.

ISBN 978 1 4052 7338 1
57741/1

Printed in Italy

EGMONT

Hello, girls!

Welcome to the pages of The Best of 70s Girls' Comics Annual. We've got some extra exciting stories for you ... creepy like 'Friends of Alison', weepy like 'Holly Takes the Plunge', full of fun like 'Sally was a Cat' and full of action like 'Bella at the Bar' and 'Beattie Beats 'Em All.'

There are heaps of things to keep you happily occupied as well ... homemade beauty tips to try, bangles, beads and bags to make, birthday horoscopes and quizzes to reveal the secret you.

This book is full of good things, just waiting to be picked out.
So, here's wishing you fun!

Your friend, *The Editor*

What's Inside ...

9

Afterwards, in the alley at the side of the cinema —

LET ME SEE WHAT WE'VE GOT HERE.

EH? YOU — YOU'RE NOT BLIND?

I'M IN SHOWBIZ, LOVE. AND IN SHOWBIZ YOU'VE GOT TO HAVE A GIMMICK — THAT'S MINE.

HEY, IT'S 50-50 — WE AGREED.

AGREEMENT? WHAT AGREEMENT? NOW PUSH OFF, KID.

WHY, YOU . . . AARGH!

HE'S NOT GETTING AWAY WITH THAT . . . OH NO!

OH, I'M TERRIBLY SORRY — I DIDN'T MEAN TO KNOCK YOU OVER.

THAT GIRL — SHE'S FROM THE MAGNIFICENT MARCONIS.

Then —

OH, NO! MY PARTNERS — THEY'VE RUMBLED ME. LOOK, YOU'VE GOT TO HELP ME — THEY'RE AFTER ME. PLEASE — TRY TO DELAY THEM FOR A MINUTE WHILE I GET AWAY.

WH — WHAT? W — WELL OKAY.

BLIMEY! SHE'S REALLY SCARED — SHE'S TAKEN OFF LIKE A BULLET. WELL, THERE'S ONLY ONE WAY TO SLOW DOWN THREE GUYS.

But —

CRIKEY — LOOK AT THAT. I FORGOT THEY WERE ACROBATS.

AT THE MIDNIGHT HOUR

GABLE INN GUEST HOUSE

"I KNEW we shouldn't have come," I said.

"Oh, shut up and don't be such a wet blanket, Jill," snapped Molly, who I suspected was beginning to have second thoughts, too.

"Wet is right. It's starting to snow harder than ever," I pointed out.

"Let's get in, then," and Molly went up the path towards the door.

"But it's empty and locked."

"Well, of course it is," sighed Molly. "It's a haunted inn, isn't it? That's why the last owners fled, terrified, in the middle of the night. That's why we're here."

"I still wish we hadn't come. I don't believe in ghosts, anyway."

"Exactly. You're a sort of referee. It was all agreed."

She was right, of course. While we'd all been discussing the haunted inn at school, Molly had said

she wouldn't mind spending [the] night there. Joan Brewer had be[en telling] her she wouldn't, and when Joa[n] went down with mumps, I'd agree[d] to stand in and make sure Moll[y] fulfilled the conditions of the be[t.] And I still wished I hadn't. I coul[d] have been at home tucked up in [a] warm bed, where Mum thought [I] was.

"We'll have to go back," I sai[d.] "We can't get in."

Molly was fiddling with a shutter and I jumped nervously as the glass of the window shattered. We looked around, but who would have heard anything above the moaning of the wind at that time of night? Midnight . . . I could hear the church clock tolling.

The inside of the place came as a bit of a shock. We'd expected the electricity to be switched off, but as we shone our torches round we saw there was no furniture anywhere, not a stick. Someone must have sent back to collect the stuff. We'd have to sleep on bare boards . . . if we were ever warm enough to sleep, though we'd brought along a couple of rugs and some food.

"You're afraid, aren't you?" said Molly, accusingly.

"Certainly not!" I flushed.

"Then why d'you want to go home?"

"It's cold and uncomfortable. I don't believe in ghosts."

And I didn't. Otherwise I wouldn't have been there. Because the ghost story of the Gable Inn was particularly chilling. The place was hundreds of years old, and way back the owners had hit on the idea of murdering their richer customers as they slept. It was a much lonelier spot then, of course, though the law finally caught up with them. Still Madame Malvern and the husband she dominated were said to roam the building, their souls unrepentant, looking for fresh victims. Brrr . . .

There was a crash from downstairs. I gave a start and caught Molly's arm.

"What's that? There's f-footsteps coming up the stairs!"

"Rubbish! It's that shutter I opened banging in the wind. I'll go and fix it."

And she'd gone before I could say "Don't bother."

I was alone in an utterly empty room. Alone except for a cupboard I now became aware of opposite me. Its double doors were painted white and I was wondering whether I should open them. There might be something we could sit on inside. The next moment, the most incredible thing happened. The cupboard doors swung open with a loud crack, as though they'd been on a spring. There was nothing inside . . . or so I thought at first. Nothing but what I can only describe as a dim light which hovered in the air, and even as I watched grew brighter till my eyes were almost dazzled. Yet I could not shut my eyes, so I saw how the light slowly resolved itself into a shape, a human shape, the unmistakable figure of a woman. She was dressed in the full skirts of two hundred years ago and her hair was piled high. There was a small black patch on her left cheek, but it was the face above all that held me. It was gaunt, the cheeks hollow and fallen away, the eyes black and small, and her expression was one of unrelenting malevolence. Then I noticed an overpowering smell, sweet and sickly, a smell of evil. The figure's arms were outstretched towards me, the claw-like hands ending in long, cruel finger nails. I could not suppress a shriek. I wondered desperately if the vision might fade, but she was coming remorselessly on. On . . . closer . . . I had no doubt I was face to face with the ghost of Madame Malvern!

Sobbing with fright, I turned and ran. Stumbling down the stairs, I shrieked again as I saw the ghostly figure of a man coming up. Madame Malvern's husband? I was trapped between them. I fainted as the figure caught my arm.

Next thing I knew, I was in Dad's car outside and there was Molly sulking in the back seat. Dad had seen my preparations earlier on and out of curiosity had followed. Molly thought I'd fixed it.

"You'd no right to spy," I protested weakly, my heart still thudding madly . . .

"You were spying on ghosts," Dad said, trying to make light of it.

When I told them about Madame Malvern, they wouldn't believe me. Dad insisted on taking me back to that room. The cupboard doors were shut, of course. There was nothing inside except the smell of mothballs, sweet and sickly . . .

When I was tucked up in bed presently Dad came to me, puffing at his pipe and dreadfully serious, as he said, "Now I want you to promise me faithfully that you'll never go to the Gable Inn again."

Well, some promises are easy to keep.

As for Molly, it was weeks before she'd speak to me again. She'd lost her bet, after all.

I'm sure that I nearly lost more—much more . . .

THE END

Fancy dressing up?

Invitations to "Fancy-Dress" parties can lead you to a lot of expense if you have to resort to hiring a costume from an agency or pay a dressmaker to run one up. Here are some ideas for you to create an outfit from garments and items you may already have, or can borrow. Even if you find you have to buy something new, it could be something you will wear again, like the leotards or cowboy boots.

GIPSY: Bright and colourful garments such as embroidered blouse, full gathered skirt with border design, small pinny, scarf, bolero and lots of bangles and beads. Wear a full petticoat under the skirt to give it more swing, and add a beribboned tambourine for an authentic finishing touch.

SOUTH SEA ISLANDER: Start off with a bikini top or "boob-tube" Add a "grass skirt" made from garden raffia stitched to a waistband or cut strips of coloured crêpe paper, using about three layers. Make coloured paper flowers and attach to wrists and ankles using elastic bands. Pin one to either side of hair and string some into a garland or "Lei" as they call them in Hawaii.

LUCKY BLACK CAT: Black leotards from a keep-fit student, plus tights, worn together with mitts, perhaps left over from a ski-ing holiday. The head can easily be made from a boy's balaclava helmet or from a tube of black jersey pulled over the head. Two "ears" can be made by pulling out and tying some of the jersey or making separate pieces and sewing them onto the hat. Paint lines on face for "whiskers". Tail is long tube of jersey or leg of old tights or stockings, stuffed and sewn on seat of leotard.

COW GIRL: Borrow a young brother's cowboy-hat and toy rifle. Find a check shirt, and a scarf to knot at your neck. The waistcoat and skirt you can fringe at the edges, or sew on matching or white fringing. Buy or borrow some boots. (cowboy-style look best), and take along the rifle, lasso or strap a holster around your waist.

CLOWN: Cut two shapes, using diagram as a guide. This you can colour with fabric paints or felt-tips. Sew together, leaving neck, cuffs and ankles open, then gathering with elastic. Sew on frill and pom-poms, adding cone-shaped hat.

TURKISH DELIGHT: Cotton scarf and hankie make a yashmak and head-dress. Bikini top and pyjama-style trousers covered with sequins, can be finished off with a brightly coloured tie. Wind gold or silver Christmas gift ribbon around ankles. Wear lots of bright bangles, too!

17

BESSIE BUNTER

18

19

GOOD NEWS FOR THE BIRTHDAY GIRL!

A BIRTHDAY is good news, whatever time of year it happens to fall! Make yours an extra-special one, and brighten up the whole year with our ideas linking things to do with your very own zodiac personality!

CAPRICORN (December 22 to January 19)

YOU are a hard-working, sensible type of person—but don't let yourself get into a rut! For a birthday present from the family, suggest something a little different—perhaps a kit connected with some kind of art or craft. You may not be obviously artistic, but Capricorns usually have a good sense of line and colour, and you'd get a lot of fun out of this. For a new hobby, this year try pebble-painting! Collect smooth, unusual or nicely-shaped pebbles whenever you are on outings or helping in the garden. Later, wash and dry them, and then use any available paints to colour them in patterns, add floral decorations, or turn them into what they already resemble. You can glue several together if you like, to make simple creatures like ducks! Use household paints, poster colours, nail varnish, paints from model-making kits.

AQUARIUS (January 20 to February 18)

INDEPENDENT type, aren't you? With quite a lot of grit and determination to back you up, too! Why not start a discussion group going among your friends or at school, with a fortnightly meeting? If fashion interests you, even if you aren't good at sewing, take a more direct interest in your own clothes. Start a project about fashion, keep a scrapbook of pictures of styles that you admire. Ask your needle-work teacher if she has any books or leaflets that give instructions for individual touches—adding big patch pockets, top-stitching along seams, embroidering or tie-dyeing—that you can use on both home-made AND ready-made clothes. Look in big department stores for useful leaflets, and watch out for interesting things like unusual belts or buttons that you could swop for the plain ones on bought clothes. Make a colour-scheme—a big wheel with every shade of the rainbow in it—and see what exciting colour combinations you can dream up, for clothes and also for decorations for your room, next time it's your turn to be smartened up.

PISCES (February 19 to March 20)

YOU HAVE a lot of patience and sympathy with those not as well off as yourself. You make an ideal pet-owner, because you have lots of affection and you take plenty of care with a creature that depends on you. If you aren't able to have one of the bigger, more interesting pets, don't give up hope or give in to sulks (rather a temptation with you!)

There may be a smaller, but still fascinating, pet that would be allowed at home—hamsters are clean and take very little space; birds make ideal pets, and if budgies are considered too noisy, there are other small birds, such as zebra finches. Fish can be colourful and interesting—you can keep cold-water tanks or tropical fish in heated aquariums. If these ideas fail, maybe you could help on Saturdays and in the holidays with other people's animals—at a stables or kennels, working in a pet shop or small local zoo, or perhaps helping with the school's animals if they keep any. But animals DO cost money, and you aren't much of a hand with savings, so if you have any long-term hopes for a really costly pet like a large breed of dog or even a pony, better start putting a little cash into a savings scheme right away! You're easily tempted to break into a piggy bank—for you, a proper bank account is much the best bet. You can open one at any post office or Trustee savings bank, and you don't have to save pounds at a time!

ARIES (March 21 to April 19)

RED is your lucky colour, so why not a red-letter year? Use red whenever you can to cheer yourself up! For a start, taking the red-letter bit seriously, treat yourself to some pink notepaper—or edge your ordinary paper with a red-ink line with felt-tipped pen, along the side of every sheet! Very smart and gay. Add a red initial to a plain blouse or skirt—simply buy some thin red cord or string, and catch it down with small stitches, to make your very own monogram. Identify your personal property with your initials in red ink, or buy some stick-on red stars, and use three or four to quickly mark your books, shoes, etc. A bottle of cheap red nail varnish makes an ideal paint to brighten up a few oddments, too—try brushing a stripe of colour along the back of a comb; giving an old string of beads a new look by painting them red; carefully colouring metal buckles on belts or shoes or your satchel (slide a piece of card under the buckle, then dabs of varnish won't get on the fabric).

But whatever you do, try not to SEE red this year! You have a quick temper, but if you count to ten (or even twenty!) before saying what's on the tip of your tongue, you'll keep your cool.

TAURUS (April 20 to May 20)

YOU are a very good organiser, because you rather enjoy giving a lot of attention to details. You might find it fun to get a little bit more involved with your youth club, school activities, Guides or church affairs. So though you are naturally rather shy, try shooting up your hand quickly, before your tummy butterflies can stop you, when volunteers are called for. Specially when the volunteer is wanted to help make lists, check names, collect subs., etc! At home, you may find yourself nagged because though you are a fairly tidy person, you don't really enjoy homely chores, and tend to skip helping with washing-up and so on. You'll earn praises instead if you offer to take on a really big job, and you'll get a lot more fun out of doing it all on your own. You've the ability to cope, if you really think about it. Start small—perhaps you could prepare Sunday lunch one week-end, or clean and re-arrange the furniture in your own room, or take younger sisters and brothers out.

GEMINI (May 21 to June 20)

BE on the look-out for opportunities to make new friends this year. You have a lively, attractive personality, and you are good at making contact with people, but you're so quick-moving that often you don't stop to develop a friendship really deeply. Result—you know plenty of people casually, but may not have a really close friend. Care about people! Start by beginning a birthday book, noting down people's birthdays, their likes and dislikes, and even notes about what colour their new clothes are. Then, when their birthday comes along, you can really make a big impression with your thoughtfulness, by choosing a bracelet or a pendant that EXACTLY matches their favourite dress! You have good fashion ideas, but tend to be careless about clothes, so they may not last as long as they should! Buy yourself plenty of cheap clothes hangers, brighten them up with stick-on transfers, or by brushing lightly with glue and winding on narrow tape, or strips of material cut from old dresses, etc. The second idea also prevents cheap metal or wooden hangers marking light material when you hang dresses and blouses up! Another idea to help keep your things tidy—tie a loop round an old bangle, and hang it up at the side of your wardrobe, inside or out, from a nail driven into the wood. Then you can put tights, belts or scarves through the bangle, and they'll keep together and won't tangle up and get spoiled!

CANCER (June 21 to July 22)

HAVE you ever tried wearing a hair-band colour-matched EXACTLY to the colour of your eyes? It can be quite fantastic! Another idea that might particularly appeal to you is to have a personal " theme " which you use as often as possible for jewellery, motifs on dresses, etc. As you are born under one of the water-signs of the zodiac, you might like to choose something like a sea-horse, a mermaid, waves or fishy shapes. You could begin a sea-shell collection, too, or start a seaside scrap book. Your personality is rather an unusual blend—you are very fond of your home and family, but you are also very much attracted to travel and far-away places! Maybe one of these days a job will take you to exciting places—at the moment, all you can do is dream about them! Don't feel guilty if you sometimes feel restless, though you know your family do everything they possibly can to make you happy and comfortable. It's just the way you are, and doesn't mean you don't love and appreciate them. You may feel less restless if you can have some kind of contact with adventurous, glamorous spots on the globe—maybe through pen-friends, or by taking a special interest in one town or country, and making a project book about it.

LEO (July 23 to August 22)

WONDER if you are feeling a bit down-in-the-mouth at the moment—maybe because a few people seem to be ganging up against you. Don't let it get you down. Try to realise that this can sometimes happen out of their jealousy. You see, most Leos are attractive, with a lot of good, enviable qualities, and luck often seems to favour them. So it's natural for others to feel jealous and act out of spite without really meaning to be unkind. Try to be big and rise above it, and take comfort from the things you are good at. You can afford to be confident in yourself—you have many qualities of a good leader, and if you trust your instincts, you can go far. This year, make a big effort to do really well in your favourite subjects. You have a very generous nature, but don't over-spend on presents for casual pals—it can be embarrassing. It sometimes makes a better impression if you spend a little time and care making gifts, or improving on inexpensive bought presents. For instance, it is fairly easy to make your own gift boxes, covering them with scraps of wallpaper and lining with cotton wool or scraps of nice fabric, and this makes a cheap, bought brooch or ring look three times as pretty! Do you have a fashion yen for pretty purses and handbags? These can cost a bomb—try making your own. You'll get bargain remnants of leather, suede, suedette and similar materials if you comb market stalls and jumble sales, and you can copy bags you already have, or buy a special paper pattern which you can find in the pattern department of any large store.

VIRGO (August 23 to September 22)

YOU'RE a bit of a fusser! Save yourself time and energy for more worthwhile things, by getting into the habit of checking important things just ONCE— then leave well alone! Listen to yourself—is your voice as attractive as it should be, or are you letting it descend into a boring nag or rise to a shrill squeak? Remember that friendships can easily be spoiled by the girl who takes too much for granted, and nags or bullies instead of coaxing —and remember, too, that a friend should be ready to listen to the other person's point of view as well as spouting forth about her own! You are normally very careful with money, and manage to stretch your pocket-money quite well. This year, why not turn your carefulness to advantage, and aim at buying something that will really bring new interest into your life? It will depend what your interests are, but you might like to have, as a target, something like a camera, a second-hand typewriter (you have lots of imagination and might like to try writing stories), or a record-player.

LIBRA (September 23 to October 22)

THIS year's holidays could be really outstanding, but don't day-dream the rest of the year away! Seems as if you could have been letting schoolwork slide a little bit just lately—right? Try to perk up your interest in "difficult" subjects by setting your own private target for marks and grades, and when you reach them, treat yourself to small gifts. Set aside 2p. a week to pay for these treats, paid out at the end of term! You have quite a sensitive personality, and you'll get a lot of personal pleasure out of paying attention to small details—such as adding a few drops of cologne when you give your hair its final rinse, or when you rinse through tights or socks. Buy inexpensive lace edging at a street market or stall, and use it on underwear for weekends and parties. Buy a length of fur or fur-fabric at a jumble sale or remnant stall, and make yourself an elegant and feminine muff for the cold weather—it's just a tube shape, big enough to put both hands in. Line it with soft material.

SCORPIO (October 23 to November 21)

YOU love secrets and mysteries, and being "different"! Why not give your birthday party a miss this year—and have an UNbirthday party at some other time of year? It makes a change, and gives you TWO very nice days to look forward to, instead of one! On your birthday, you might like to turn the tables and give your mum tea in bed as a surprise and a way of saying "thank you for having me!" And instead of a party, treat yourself and perhaps your best friend to a visit to somewhere interesting locally, in connection with a favourite hobby, sport or pastime. Interestingly, your birthstone is the topaz, not an expensive

stone, and as it can be pink, yellow or white, it gives you a good choice of colours! It might be fun to have a ring or a pendant set with a topaz, as a birthday or Christmas gift from the family, or you could save up for one for yourself. Another idea which is unusual and might suit you is to search out a book on semi-precious stones in any library, and find a coloured illustration of topaz, which is usually a very pretty mineral, and use this to copy to make a poster-sized picture for your bedroom. Pick up the main colour for things like lamp-shade, beside rug, dressing-table ornaments, slippers, etc., many of which you can make yourself.

SAGITTARIUS (November 22 to December 21)

SOME say that yours is the luckiest sign in the whole zodiac, so make sure you USE all the good fortune that comes your way this year! Be on the look-out for opportunities of every kind—they seldom come twice! Maybe you feel that your parents chose a very boring name for you—but there is nothing against you choosing your own middle name if you want to! All you have to do is pick another name that you feel expresses your personality, and then make your friends use it! Use it as a middle name, and eventually if you really prefer it, maybe your family will start using it too, and you can finally drop your original Christian name if you want. You are NOT naturally a tidy person, but living in a mess is bad for your frame of mind—it's so depressing to wade through a jumble of dirty socks, magazines, half-completed jig-saws and so on on your way to bed each night! If you can't put things away neatly, at least have a place in your room where everything goes. Beg cardboard boxes from shops (supermarkets and sweet-shops usually have a surplus), cover them in scraps of left-over wallpaper or fabric cut from outworn clothes, and store different things in each—comics, belts, shoes, games and so forth. Put the boxes on shelves, on top of the wardrobe, or under the bed! You have a friendly, nice nature—we think you might enjoy choosing one day each month to give an unexpected treat to someone in the family, a friend or neighbour. It needn't cost money—just your time and thought. Take an elderly neighbour a sample cake from the batch you bake, polish all your father's shoes, make a friend a pretty head-band out of dress-making scraps, arrange garden flowers in a pretty vase for your mother's bedside table.

Called to Save

NINA COOKE WAS THE BEST DIVER IN HER SCHOOL. AND SHE WAS DETERMINED TO WIN THE INTER-SCHOOLS CHAMPION-SHIPS.

I THINK YOU HAVE A REAL CHANCE OF WINNING, NINA. THAT'S WHY I'VE GIVEN YOU ACCESS TO THE SCHOOL'S POOL AT ALL TIMES.

THANK YOU HEADMISTRESS.

I STILL CAN'T GET USED TO SWIMMING HERE WHEN THE POOL'S EMPTY. IT — IT'S SO SPOOKY.

BUT ENOUGH OF THAT. I'VE GOT TWO HOURS SOLID TRAINING AHEAD OF ME.

HEY, I'M NOT ALONE, AFTER ALL. BUT WHO IS THAT GIRL ON THE HIGH DIVE?

WOW, WHAT A DIVE. THAT WAS PERFECT. I WISH I WAS THAT GOOD!

THAT'S FUNNY — SHE SHOULD HAVE SURFACED BY NOW.

WHAT? THERE'S NO SIGN OF HER. AND THE WATER'S AS CLEAR AS GLASS.

But then —

THERE SHE IS — GOING INTO A CHANGING CUBICLE. BUT HOW DID SHE GET OUT OF THE WATER WITHOUT ME SEEING HER?

HEY, THERE! WHO ARE YOU? WHAT ARE YOU DOING HERE?

26

Friends of Alison

IT had been a lovely dream, Alison remembered afterwards. She could see herself running through long grass, laughing up at the sun, feeling so happy to think she belonged somewhere.

There were voices, too. Happy, laughing voices which called to each other: "Alison's home! Alison's home . . . home . . ."

Now, there was another voice, kind but sounding much nearer, more down to earth.

"Wake up, Alison, dear! Only another mile or two, and then the train will be stopping at Molefield Junction!"

Her mother smiled at Alison. "I let you sleep for as long as I could. You seemed so peaceful."

Alison opened her mouth, then shut it again. She wasn't sure she wanted to tell her mother about the dream, not yet, anyway. Home was a place they hadn't known for a long time, not since Alison's father died when she was quite tiny.

"I'll start getting our cases

down from the rack," she blurted out, secretly glad of something to do.

"Molefield is a dear little place," Mother was saying. "Your daddy and I always loved it when we were young."

"Of course," she went on, "I suppose it's changed a lot, but I expect Maydew Cottage is still the same. It's a bit out of the way, but it'll be all right for the dressmaking job I've got with the boutique in the next town. Come along, dear."

There weren't any taxis at the station, so Alison and her mother had to start walking. Soon Alison's arms began to ache, and the bottom of her jeans were wet with splashes of mud from the narrow country road. She hoped Maydew Cottage would be worth the trouble.

"There it is!" her mother cried out at last, as a red tiled roof peeped above the top of the hedge. Alison could see a tiny window set into the roof, too, and thought joyfully of the attic bedroom Mum had promised her.

"It's perfect, Mum!" she exclaimed, hurrying along and almost forgetting the heavy suitcases she was carrying.

"What's that place?" she asked suddenly, pointing to a larger building in the distance, mostly hidden by the thick trees and bushes which grew round it. "It looks like a school, or something."

"That's Woodview Manor," Mother told her, turning a key slowly in the lock. "I believe it must still be empty, even after all these years."

She could see Woodview Manor from the little window, too.

A few of the windows seemed to be broken, and there were weeds and creeper trailing everywhere—but it wasn't lonely and forgotten, she was sure. And she could almost hear voices, calling—

"Alison! See, Alison's home . . . Alison's home . . . home . . ."

"Alison!" It was Mum's voice again. "Come downstairs and help me unpack, dear! The furniture van will be arriving soon."

Later on, after the removal men had hauled furniture around, grumbling about the steep stairs, the uneven floors and the narrow doorways at Maydew Cottage, Alison looked out towards Woodview Manor again. Moonlight made it seem different, more magical, and she could see some of the windows winking across at her, as if the house itself was her friend.

Alison gave a deep sigh and snuggled down into bed. It sounded funny, having a house for a friend . . . She did wish she had someone to talk to, someone who would understand. But having a house was still nice and comforting, somehow.

And as she fell asleep, she could hear the voices again.

"Alison's home . . . Alison's home . . ."

It was quite a few days before Alison found time to visit Woodview Manor. Hundreds of spiders had spun their webs in the thick bushes, their fine threads brushing Alison's face and hands as she pushed her way nearer.

Now she could see that there were bits missing in the brickwork, with showers of rust softly falling down from a broken drain-pipe. It must have been empty for a long time, just as her mother had said. And, yet—

"Ready! I'm ready, Sally! Bet you can't find me this time!"

Someone was calling quite near to Alison, just behind her, it seemed.

"Ssssh, don't give me away," the voice hissed, closer this time. "Sally is

always best at hide and seek . . ."

There was a tug at Alison's sleeve, and she turned to see a boy just a little younger than herself, she guessed, with thick, brown curly hair and a crinkly smile.

He wiped his hands down the front of his jersey. "Have you been looking for birds' nests as well?" he asked.

"Well, we've only just moved to Molefield," Alison began, "just my Mum and me, and——"

She stopped, hearing footsteps scuffling towards them. A long pair of arms parted two thick branches, and a girl's face appeared, looking pleased with herself.

"Got you!" she cried triumphantly. "Who said I couldn't find you, Podge?"

★   ★   ★

"It was my fault for talking too loud," Alison apologised. "I didn't mean to spoil your game."

"Podge isn't much good at the game, anyway," laughed Sally, her dark curls dancing in the breeze. "You're the girl who's come to live at Maydew Cottage, aren't you? What's your name?"

"Alison," said Alison faintly, feeling surprised that Podge and Sally appeared to know something about her already. "But, I-I thought nobody lived here any more."

Sally laughed again. "That's silly! We're here, aren't we? Me, Podge, Mother and Daddy. At least," she added, "three of us. Daddy's away at the moment."

"Let's play something else," suggested Podge. "What about rounders?"

"All right, we can go into the back garden," Sally agreed. "Come on, Alison."

Linking arms with Alison, Sally led her around the side of the house, past two enormous french windows. They weren't broken, Alison noticed, and they had long, velvet curtains hanging inside.

"Podge can bowl first," announced Sally. "We've only got one bat, so drop it as soon as you've hit the ball, right?"

"Right," smiled Alison, looking around the big garden in delight. She had been right about this place, she told herself. Anyone who thought it was bleak and empty had just got the wrong idea. It was all a mistake.

"Run, Alison, run!" yelled Sally, as Alison hit the ball wildly. "Don't give Podge a chance to catch you before you get home!"

Then Alison was running through the grass, laughing happily, with the sun on her face.

"Alison's home!" Sally shouted gleefully, a minute or two later. "Hard luck, Podge! Alison's home! Alison's home!"

Alison stared hard at Sally, her face creasing into a huge smile. She had never believed in dreams coming true before . . .

That night, Alison decided to ask her mother about Woodview Manor.

"It used to be owned by some people in the village," Mum told her, stitching busily. "They were sort of distant cousins of your daddy's, so I believe, although he never met them."

Mother paused, and put down her sewing, staring thoughtfully into the fire.

"Their father went abroad and lost all his money on some business deal, I think. The family were left alone, so

they had to move soon afterwards."

"Go on, Mum," begged Alison, hugging her knees.

"There's not much more to tell. It seemed the father had sold the Deeds of the Manor to pay off his debts, and that was that."

"And what about the people in the house afterwards?"

"Well," she sighed, "they swore the Manor was haunted."

"Haunted?" repeated Alison huskily.

*   *   *

"That's right. It may have been imagination, what with the Manor being so large, and noises echoing. But the people said they heard voices in the garden, and in the hall. They were sure it sounded like children, but there weren't any children around at all. The Manor had been turned into offices by then, you see."

"And doesn't anyone live there now? It's completely empty?"

"Yes, it's been empty for a long, long time," said Mother. "Don't you remember me telling you?"

"Yes," said Alison slowly. "I remember."

She wished she could tell her mother that she'd got the wrong idea, too, made the same mistake as everyone else.

Each time Alison went to Woodview Manor, Podge and Sally were waiting. Sometimes they played games, other times they made a camp in the grounds, or just lazed around and talked.

*   *   *

Once or twice she brought them presents—a notebook for Podge when he went bird-watching, and some hair-slides for Sally.

"We'll have to give you something, too," insisted Sally. "Then we can put them in our secret place, by the front gate. Come on, we'll show you!"

"I found the secret place!" Podge informed Alison proudly. "One of the paving stones wobbled one day, and it made me fall and hurt my knee."

Sally interrupted: "And then I found there was a bit of space underneath where the stone hadn't been set in the ground properly. It was my idea to make it our secret place."

Podge pouted and heaved up the stone, so that Sally could slip her hand inside.

"We put all our really special things in here," she said, groping around. "Well, Podge has only got bits of birds' eggs, conkers and things. A load of rubbish, really."

"No, it's not!" protested

Podge, nudging Sally indignantly. What about the stamp on that envelope I found? That's worth a lot of money, I bet! That's what I'm going to give to Alison!''

''Oh, no!'' he wailed. ''Sally, you've gone and pushed it right under the next stone, and I can't get it out!''

A woman's voice called from inside the house. ''Podge! Sally! Here a minute!''

''Don't worry, Podge,'' said Alison hastily, seeing his bottom lip quivering. ''I'll get the envelope for you and keep it safe till next time.''

''Podge! Sally!'' the voice called again, more urgently.

''We'll have to go,'' said Sally, beginning to drag Podge towards the Manor. ''Be seeing you, Alison.''

Lying full stretch on the ground, Alison could see the edge of the envelope, but it was wedged too tightly for her fingers to pull at it.

''This is hopeless,'' she muttered at last. ''I'll have to bring Mum's tweezers tomorrow.''

She walked back to Maydew Cottage, feeling strangely troubled.

Woodview Manor didn't look quite so magical from her bedroom either. The windows weren't winking at her in the moonlight, and she could hear someone sobbing in the darkness, the sadness drifting across the countryside towards her . . . .

As soon as it was light, Alison threw back the bedclothes and peered out of the window. Woodview Manor seemed colder, lonelier than ever. She could still picture it as she washed herself at the cold water tap in the bathroom, got dressed and crept downstairs, treading carefully so as not to wake her mother.

Her hands trembled as she took the big tweezers from a drawer in the sewing machine cabinet, and she tried hard to blink back the falling tears.

''As soon as I get Podge's envelope, everything will be all right again,'' she kept whispering, all the way to the Manor. ''That's what changed everything, made it all so horrid . . . .''

She stopped, hearing Podge and Sally talking together.

''Don't cry, Sally,'' Podge was pleading tearfully.

''You heard what Mummy said,'' wept Sally. ''We've got to go away, leave our home and move somewhere else.''

Podge was crying now. Tears splashed down his fat cheeks and made his eyes pink at the edges.

''I'll look after you and Mummy. And we'll come back to Woodview Manor some day.''

Alison couldn't bear it.

''You can't go!'' she cried out, desperately pushing her way towards them. Just tell me what I can do to help, that's all!''

But Podge and Sally were walking very slowly into the house, with their arms around each other and still crying, not even noticing that Alison was there at all.

She hurried after Sally and Podge through a long, tiled hall, her shoes tip-tapping as she ran. Still, Podge and Sally were going away, up a wide, curling staircase, still with their arms round each other and crying, till they were out of sight.

Alison brushed away her tears and looked harder. There were great gaps in the stairs and the walls. Giant cobwebs on the ceiling and lumps of plaster covering the tiled floor with a fine powder, grey and undisturbed, except for the prints of her own footsteps.

''No!'' she screamed out. ''No, it isn't true! It's all part of the same mistake, the same horrible mistake!''

Alison rushed blindly outside and fell to her knees, clawing frantically at the clumps of weeds spreading over the loose paving stone, the Secret Place that had belonged to her, Podge and Sally.

''Everything's got to be all

Friends of Alison

right,' she told herself fiercely, hardly feeling her grazed knuckles. ''I promised Podge, everything would be all right.''

Podge's envelope was still there, wedged underneath the stone. The tweezers shook in her hand, but she gripped tightly and started to tug. Her eyes were still blurred and her head ached. But she was beginning to feel happier.

Podge and Sally could start laughing again, very soon. She could hear them calling again, in the distance.

''Alison! Alison . . . .''

''Alison?'' A smooth hand brushed hair back from Alison's forehead and a voice spoke anxiously. ''Alison, dear, how are you feeling?''

Alison opened her eyes, looking up at the sloping ceiling above her bed.

''You were lucky the station master was walking his dog near Woodview Manor,'' someone else said.

The burly face of a big policeman became clearer.

''And you'll be pleased to know we took those deeds to the local solicitor's office, so that the owners can be contacted. How did you know where they were, after so long?''

''Deeds?'' Alison repeated vaguely. ''I don't know what you're talking about——.''

''The deeds inside the envelope,'' the policeman explained patiently. ''The deeds everyone thought had been sold years ago to pay business debts.''

''You remember, Alison,'' her mother said gently. ''I told you about the family who lived at the Manor when we first moved here. The children who were your daddy's distant cousins, and who had to go abroad.''

Alison leant back on her pillows, smiling to herself. She had rescued Podge's envelope—the one with his much-prized stamp—out of the Secret Place, and now it was safe. That was all that mattered. Woodview Manor would come alive again, she was certain. She fell asleep, happy at last.

Next day, Alison's mother burst in through the door,

waving a slip of paper. ''Your Uncle Toby and Aunt Sally are coming back to Molefield!'' she cried. ''The Post Office have just sent over the telegram to say they'll be arriving late tonight!''

Alison's heart leapt.

''Who's Uncle Toby and Aunt Sally, Mum?''

''Those cousins of daddy's, the children who once lived at Woodview Manor and who moved away over forty years ago. The deeds you found were proof that their father had still owned the Manor when he made his will and left the house to them. Now they can come home, and once Uncle Toby has settled everything with the lawyers, we'll have a big family around us, all at once!''

''And we'll never be alone again,'' Alison sighed happily. ''How lovely.'' Then she added: ''But won't they mind about the ghosts?''

''I shouldn't think it would worry them,'' Mum answered, and she chuckled. ''After all, it was their home, a long time ago, before ghosts were even mentioned!''

''Yes,'' agreed Alison. ''Yes, that's true.'' And she began looking forward to seeing Uncle Toby and Aunt Sally, watching the clock tick the hours away and wondering if time had ever passed quite so slowly.

At last, a car engine purred to a halt outside Maydew Cottage.

''It's them!'' Alison ex-

claimed in excitement, and flung open the door, sending a pool of yellow light onto the path outside.

Uncle Toby strode towards her, a tall, broad-shouldered man with eyes that twinkled brightly and a trim moustache. His face had a few wrinkles, and his dark, curly hair was flecked with grey. But his crinkly smile was still the same.

''Podge!'' Alison breathed. She hesitated for one moment, then ran forward, flinging her arms wide.

''Podge,'' she whispered again, leaning her head against his tweed jacket, ''I knew you and Sally hadn't gone away, not really!''

His bright eyes widened with joy and wonder as he looked closely at Alison's upturned face.

''Alison!'' he cried. ''Alison, our friend, is it really you?''

''Sally!'' he called out towards the smartly-dressed lady who was just coming up the path. ''Sally, come and see who's here! You'll never believe it!''

Sally smiled her old, familiar smile at Alison.

''Yes, I would, Toby. You and I have had to wait, but now we really can go home with Alison.''

They went indoors together. And across the woodland, through the thick bushes, the window of Woodview Manor began winking again.

THE END

SEE YOURSELF~ IN YOUR TRUE COLOURS

COLOURS have more power as luck-bringers than most of us realise—and if you don't believe it, just think how great you feel wearing that special dress or outfit which always seems to make nice things happen.

So why not try our Personality Quiz, and find out what lucky colours could mean to YOU!

A) What do you think should go in this vase—

1) An arrangement of feathers and bullrushes?
2) An old-fashioned aspidistra?
3) An indoor rubber plant?
4) Tall chrysanthemums?
5) Painted leaves and ferns?

B) Who do you think would send this birthday card to you—

1) Your Mum or Dad?
2) A best friend?
3) An elderly Aunty, or Grandma?
4) Somebody who does not know you that well?
5) A friend of the family?

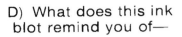

D) What does this ink blot remind you of—

1) A beetle?
2) A cloud?
3) A frog?
4) A rocket?
5) A map of some undiscovered island?

C) What do you think this could be—

1) A sample of curtain material?
2) A piece of dress fabric?
3) A wall-hanging?
4) A calendar picture?
5) A panel of scenery for a fairy tale production?

E) Where do you think this oriental lady belongs—

1) On a chocolate box?
2) As a greetings card?
3) On an advert for a Chinese restaurant?
4) As a symbol for a large airline?
5) On your bedroom wall, maybe?

G) Which design would you put in this stained-glass window—

1) A religious scene?
2) A mosaic pattern in different colours?
3) A design of leaves and flowers?
4) A plain centre, with ornamental lettering around the edge?
5) Exotic birds and beautiful butterflies?

F) Suppose you had to give a name to this water colour painting. Would it be—

1) Sunset?
2) Water colours?
3) Reflections?
4) Daybreak?
5) Peace?

H) What message do you think would go with this painting—

1) Get well soon?
2) Be my Valentine?
3) Congratulations on your 21st birthday?
4) With love on Mother's Day?
5) Best wishes on your Wedding Anniversary?

I) Finally, have a look at this young girl's work of art. How do you think the child felt about painting it?

1) Happy?
2) Disgusted?
3) Interested?
4) Bored?
5) Impatient?

NOW

Now, check your score on our table to see which letter most of your answers come under.

	1		2		3		4		5	
Question A:	1	D	2	E	3	A	4	B	5	C
Question B:	1	A	2	E	3	C	4	B	5	D
Question C:	1	E	2	B	3	D	4	C	5	A
Question D:	1	A	2	C	3	D	4	B	5	C
Question E:	1	E	2	B	3	A	4	B	5	D
Question F:	1	E	2	C	3	D	4	C	5	A
Question G:	1	E	2	D	3	A	4	B	5	D
Question H:	1	B	2	B	3	D	4	E	5	A
Question I:	1	A	2	C	3	D	4	B	5	D
					E		C	4		

Conclusions...

MAINLY A. Bet this isn't the first time you've been told that you're a real dreamer. To overcome the shy side of your personality you could wear almost any shade of blue, and this will attract other people to your natural kindness and quiet, thoughtful nature. Lilac would also bring you luck in any kind of examination or interview, especially if you could wear a piece of jewellery with silver or grey in the design. Dark or very vivid colours would be too overpowering for your gentle character, so they wouldn't be much good as luck-bringers!

* * *

MOSTLY B. You're always full of energy, bouncing with life and wanting to be where the action is. And, as you like to be noticed, bright colours are definitely for you, especially red and orange. Another luck-bringer is yellow which would chime with your sunny outlook and bright sense of humour. At times you find it difficult to slow down and concentrate, particularly when you're alone. That's when autumn browns and golds will help you relax, either in the clothes you wear or perhaps a bedroom colour scheme. Try it and see!

* * *

MOSTLY C. Mystery and imagination are your key words, and most deep, rich shades are the lucky colours for you. Mauve is probably a favourite with you already, but you could also rely on crimson or turquoise when you want to make a good impression with your intelligence and determination. Black or beige are also luck-bringers when worn with any of your lucky colours, and, as you are also a nature lover at heart, anything with a bold, floral pattern would help you to smile and take life less seriously at times. White flowers will always bring you luck, too.

* * *

MOSTLY D. Your feeling and interest in Art and Design means that you have a wider range of lucky colours than girls in other groups. Nearly all unusual shades and patterns will tune in with your search for new ideas and things to try, but green is the luckiest colour of all for you, especially if there is some beige or brown to blend in with the colour scheme. And when you choose jewellery or any kind of ornament, remember that anything made from wood will also bring you luck. How about a wooden lucky mascot?

* * *

MOSTLY E. Pink is definitely your luckiest colour, because it brings out your generous and warm-hearted personality for everyone to see! But disappointments come easily to you, so choose tan or peachey-orange when you need to strengthen your determination to try again and cheer yourself up. Cream and light brown are also colours to give your self-confidence a boost and help you conquer any feelings of unease and restlessness. You will always feel happiest with feminine, dainty designs and a charm bracelet or a charm worn on a chain would be particularly lucky to you.

Sally was a Cat

How to make

Baubles,
Bangles
& Beads

Necklace knitted in twine and string, and knotted at intervals.

Necklace knitted in wool and lurex mixture.

44

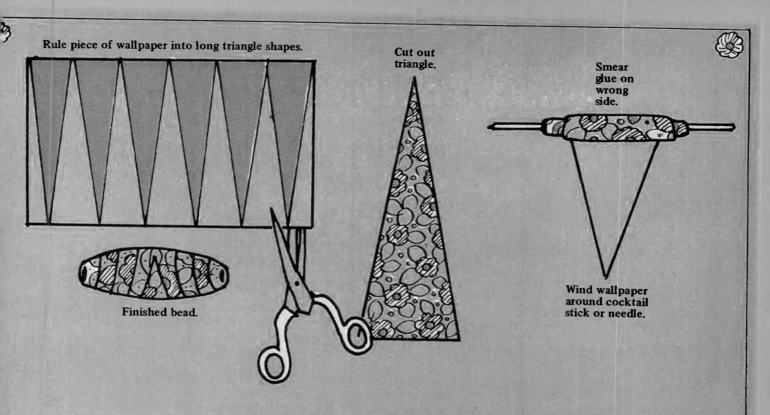

Rule piece of wallpaper into long triangle shapes.

Cut out triangle.

Smear glue on wrong side.

Finished bead.

Wind wallpaper around cocktail stick or needle.

Want to make yourself a necklace for next to nothing? Then just find some scraps of wallpaper — the washable or vinyl sort is best — some glue and scissors and you're ready to start.

First, cut pieces of wallpaper at a depth of about 8" (20 cm). (The width doesn't really matter, but you may find it helpful to know that the wider your piece of paper, the more beads you'll get. Narrow bits can be used just as well). Then, rule off in long, thin triangles as shown in our diagram, about 1" (2.4 cm) at the top. This will give you beads 1" wide, so, if you like, you can vary the size yourself.

When you've cut out the triangles, dab glue on to the wrong side of the paper and wind round a cocktail stick or old knitting needle, working from the broadest end to the tip. Then slip off the cocktail stick—and you've made your first bead! Make as many as you think you'll need for your necklace—about 35—40 is a good number—and leave to dry thoroughly, at least overnight.

You'll then find that the beads have dried quite hard and feel rather like wood to touch. You can thread your beads as they are, or paint them with nail varnish. That's a fiddly job, but loads of fun!

And if you want to look really special, you could make a bracelet, a headband, hair-slides using the beads wound round ordinary grips—almost anything you like! You can also improvise with paper from *glossy* magazines! But ask mum first before cutting out!

Or, have you ever tried knitting a necklace? It's so easy, with a ball of sparkly wool—something like Twilley's "Goldfingering"—or ordinary 3 ply or 4 ply wool used with a reel of lurex thread which you can buy in most wool shops.

Using no. 10 needles, cast on 8 stitches and knit in garter stitch, (every row plain), for about 35 inches, (89 cm). The more you knit, the longer your necklace will be, so it's up to you. Cast off, leaving quite a long thread of wool.

Now, hold one end of your knitting and twist it round and round with your other hand to get a spiral effect—just like we do with the curly streamers at Christmas-time. Then all you have to do is sew the ends together, using the long thread of wool at the end of your casting-off and put on your new necklace, Couldn't be easier, could it?

But if you don't want anything sparkly, you could try using garden twine or string, instead, casting on 6 stitches and using no. 9 needles. There are lots of gorgeous colours to choose from and you can buy it in hardware shops or department stores. And, if you want to change the design, you can tie knots in the strip of knitting every 3 inches (8 cm) or so. You'll be really surprised how great it will look with your holiday outfits!

BEATTIE BEATS 'EM ALL!

BEATTIE BROWN WAS A YOUNG COCKNEY ORPHAN, TRAVELLING FROM PLACE TO PLACE WITH STRAY CATS AS HER ONLY COMPANIONS. BEATTIE WAS ALSO AN OUTSTANDING ATHLETE, AND ONE DAY —

FLAT BROKE, I AM, MOGGIES. BUT NOW WE'VE CLAPPED EYES ON THEM GIRLS OUT WITH THEIR COACH, RECKON IT WON'T BE LONG AFORE I'M ON THE TRACK AGAIN, AN' WINNING PRIZES! WHAT D'YOU THINK OF THAT?

BET YOU'D BE GLAD TO HAVE ME IN YOUR TEAM FOR A BIT, GUV'NOR. I'M PROPER NIPPY ON ME FEET, ONCE I GETS GOING!

HUH! I'M NOT IN THE HABIT OF ENLISTING CLUB MEMBERS AT FIRST SIGHT!

THOUGHT I'D GIVE YOU FIRST OFFER ANYWAY CHUM. BUT SEEIN' AS YOU'VE TURNED ME DOWN, I'LL MAKE OUT ON ME OWN. YOU WON'T ARF KICK YOURSELF, THEN!

CHEEKY YOUNG BRAT! I'D RETIRE IF I THOUGHT MY ATHLETES WERE NO BETTER THAN YOU!

YOU'D BEST START FILLIN' IN FORMS FOR YOUR PENSION. YOU'RE TRAINING FOR A SPORTS MEETING, AN' WHEN I FIND OUT WHERE THAT IS, I'LL SHOW YOU I MEANS WHAT I SAYS!

YOU HAVEN'T A HOPE OF ENTERING ANY COMPETITION ROUND HERE. GET GOING!

A RIGHT OLE SNOBBY-BOOTS, THAT GEEZER IS. BUT ALL I'VE GOT TO DO IS FIND OUT WHERE THIS CONTEST IS BEING HELD...

Further down the road...

THIS MUST BE THE PLACE, AN' IF I TAGS ON TO THE END OF THAT QUEUE, P'RAPS THE FELLA AT THE GATE WON'T SAY NOTHING... IT'S WORTH HAVING A BASH!

YOUR CLUB MEMBERSHIP CARD, PLEASE, MISSIE.

ER, SORRY, GAFFER, I MUST HAVE DROPPED IT SOMEWHERE. EITHER THAT, OR IT GOT LOST IN THE POST.

THIS YOUNG HORROR SAID SHE COULD GIVE MY TEAM A BEATING! TELL HER TO BUZZ OFF!

TAKE NO NOTICE OF THAT BLOKE, MISTER. I WOULDN'T BE IN HIS SNOOTY CLUB, NOT FOR A SHARE IN A GOLD MINE!

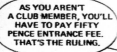

AS YOU AREN'T A CLUB MEMBER, YOU'LL HAVE TO PAY FIFTY PENCE ENTRANCE FEE. THAT'S THE RULING.

IT AIN'T BLOOMIN' FAIR. THEM FOLKS THAT'S WELL OFF GETS IN FOR FREE, AN' HERE'S ME, PROPER SKINT, AN' CAN'T GET PAST THE DOOR. A PERISHIN' SWIZZ, I CALLS IT!

Sadly, Beattie went away.

LOOKS LIKE WE'RE IN THE SOUP THIS TIME, GANG. AIN'T EVEN GOT ENOUGH LOLLY TO GET A CUPPA TEA FOR MESELF, AN' A SPOT OF MILK FOR YOU LOT.

MIND WHERE THOSE CATS ARE GOING, LOVE. IT ONLY NEEDS ONE OF THEM BOTTLES TO GO OVER, AN' THERE'LL BE BROKEN GLASS FOR MILES AROUND.

STONE THE CROWS! LEMONADE BOTTLES, JUST WAITING FOR ME TO TAKE 'EM INTO THE CAFE, AN' GET CASH ON 'EM. I'D BETTER LOOK SHARP, AFORE SOMEONE ELSE GETS THE SAME IDEA . . .

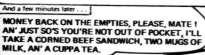

And a few minutes later . . .

MONEY BACK ON THE EMPTIES, PLEASE, MATE! AN' JUST SO'S YOU'RE NOT OUT OF POCKET, I'LL TAKE A CORNED BEEF SANDWICH, TWO MUGS OF MILK, AN' A CUPPA TEA.

DON'T SAY THEM FOLKS FROM THE SPORTS CENTRE HAVE BEEN DUMPING STUFF OUTSIDE MY PLACE, AGAIN. I'VE GOT ABOUT FOUR CRATE LOADS PILED UP AT THE BACK ALREADY.

EH? BUT I THOUGHT THESE BOTTLES WERE YOURS.

THE SNACK BAR AT THE SPORTS CENTRE GETS CROWDED. PEOPLE GO OUTSIDE, TO HAVE THEIR DRINKS IN PEACE, AND LEAVE THE BOTTLES NEAR MY CAFE. COME AN' TAKE A LOOK.

CRIPES! SOME PEOPLE MUST BE ROLLING IN CASH, LEAVING ALL THIS LOT LYING AROUND!

IT'S TOO MUCH BOTHER FOR THEM TO RETURN THEM, LASS, AND I'M ALWAYS TOO BUSY TO TAKE 'EM MYSELF.

LOOK, CHUM, I'LL DO A DEAL. YOU GIVE ME AN' THE CATS A BIT O' GRUB, AN' I'LL CLEAR YOUR YARD. THAT WAY, WE'D BE SWOPPING FAVOURS!

RIGHT-OH, DUCKS. I'LL GET THE MISSUS TO SET YOU UP WITH EGG AN' CHIPS IN THE KITCHEN, THEN YOU CAN START WORK.

Soon . . .

JUST THE JOB, THIS IS, MOGGIES. TUCK IN, THEN WE'LL GET BACK TO THAT SPORTS CENTRE. AN' THIS TIME, I AIN'T BEING STOPPED BY NO ONE!

When Beattie had finished her meal . . .

COME ON, ME OLE MATES! DON'T WANT THE SNACK BAR GOING BUST 'COS THERE AIN'T ENOUGH BOTTLES TO GO ROUND, DO WE?

WHAT ARE YOU DOING BACK HERE? I THOUGHT YOU'D BEEN SENT AWAY ONCE!

CAN'T STOP FOR A CHIN-WAG, MISTER. THERE'LL BE A RIGHT RUMPUS IF I DON'T GET THIS LOT OVER TO THE SNACK BAR, TAKE IT FROM ME!

HOLLY TAKES THE PLUNGE!

"YOU'VE got a nerve, Jeff Framley—asking my grandmother to lend you the Gaydon family diaries!"

Holly Allan's cheeks burned with anger. "My family worked for the Gaydons right back from early Georgian days when Gaydon Grange was built. And my Nan was housekeeper to Sir William until he died. She was the only help he could afford to keep in the house by then, poor old man!"

"I know that, Holly!" Jeff spoke gently. "The family papers were all he had to leave her in his will. I'm interested in the history of the Gaydons, now that MY family lives in the house; that's why I wanted to see the diaries. And Dad says they have been helpful by giving him ideas how to renovate the Grange."

A roaring bonfire spread a glow over the snowy garden and hundreds of Chinese lanterns shone merrily from the trees

"Dad says! Dad says!" parroted Holly rudely. "Haven't you got any ideas of your own?"

Jeff bit his lip. "Why do you dislike Dad so much—and me?" he asked, bluntly.

"Your father may be rich enough to buy the Grange, but he'll never belong there, not like the Gaydons did. You're—you're gate-crashers!" Holly felt the gathering tears stinging her eyes. She turned away abruptly. She would not let Jeff Framley see her cry.

On her way home from school, Holly passed the massive iron gates of Gaydon Grange, with the family arms carved into the stone archway above. She felt her grandmother had betrayed the Gaydons, dead and gone, by letting Jeff handle the diaries. In fact, Holly had only found out about it when she had asked her grandmother to let her browse through them again. Holly watched a builder's lorry rumbling down the gravel drive.

"Trust a moneybags like Gerald Framley to ruin a gracious old house by turning it into a modern monstrosity! I bet he's having all the rooms decorated with washable papers in hideous colours," muttered Holly.

The sky was leaden with threatening snow, and the ground still ankle-deep from the last fall. Holly pulled the hood of her anorak down farther over her face, and wiggled her fingers, still chilly in spite of her warm woollen mitts.

"Brrr! It IS cold! The lake in the Grange grounds will be frozen hard. If the estate still belonged to Sir William, I could have been skating on the lake right now!" Holly sighed. The kindly old man had given her a free run of the house and grounds when her grandmother worked for him.

Holly's resentment against the new owners gathered momentum as she stamped along, crunching her boots into the hard snow as if she were grinding the Framleys underfoot. She had come to think of the Grange as hers: and now it had been snatched from her.

Jeff Framley, reaching the Grange gates, paused to watch Holly vanish over the brow of the hill. He sighed. "Holly by name and Holly by nature. She's determined to show her prickles. I just can't get through to her." He thrust his hands into his pockets and began to stride up the drive. "But maybe the party will tempt her to call a truce."

During Jeff's research into the Gaydon family history, he had discovered that, in the early days, it had been the custom on Twelfth Night to throw a large party for all the youngsters living nearby. The tradition had died out when only old Sir William was left in the vast house; but Mr. Framley was only too delighted at Jeff's suggestion that it should be revived that very January.

※ ※ ※

Jeff and his mother sent invitations to all the schools within miles, and, next morning, Holly arrived in class to find all her friends buzzing with excitement over the party.

"Huh! I suppose the Framleys want to show off!" snapped Holly. "Of course, it won't be as good as the super parties the Gaydons used to throw years ago.'

"That was before our time," frowned her friend, Dee. "You're the only one of us who's been lucky enough to enjoy the Grange and its grounds lately."

Holly flushed guiltily. Dee was right. She had been the only child who had had the opportunity to skate on the lake and to swim there in the summer.

"I think it's terrific of Jeff's Dad to lay on this do for us," said Dee, firmly. "And I bet it'll be a really super party if Jeff has anything to do with it."

"Anyhow, I don't think I'll bother to go to their silly old party," muttered Holly.

However, as the days passed, Holly could not ignore the mounting excitement. It was infectious! The girls and boys were checking their skates and making toboggans. With the heavy snowfall and the freezing weather, they'd be able to enjoy some winter sports on Twelfth Night.

"I'm just dying to see the inside of the house, too," chattered Dee, full of enthusiasm. "I hear Mr. Framley has spent thousands on it! It must look fantabulous!"

As the night of the party approached, Holly's resolution to stand aloof began to melt. Her family thought her foolish to pass up such a kind invitation; and, at last, Holly's curiosity to see the Grange once more, and to enjoy the skating, overcame her obstinacy.

When she arrived at the house early that evening, she could scarcely stifle her surprise as Jeff led her along the wide hall from the front door to the terrace at the rear of the house.

Through the open doors she could see that the rooms were tastefully re-decorated in the same colours as the architect had used when the house was built in the early eighteen-hundreds. The brocade curtains were of the original pattern and colouring. "Mr. Framley must have had them specially woven!" thought Holly.

The portraits of the ancestral Gaydons were cleaned and restored to their former splendour. All the shabbiness and disrepair caused by the Gaydons' failing fortunes had been swept away, to leave the house as beautiful as it had ever been. Of course, only a wealthy man could have lavished money on this scale; but Holly could not blind herself to the fact that money alone could not have brought about such a perfect renovation. It had taken loving care and deep respect for the gracious old house.

Perversely, this made Holly all the more resentful of the Framleys. She would NOT accept them as belonging to Gaydon Grange! They were interlopers!

Holly joined the crowd of happy youngsters on the terrace. A roaring bonfire spread a warm glow over the snow-covered sunken garden. Hundreds of Chinese lanterns bobbed merrily from the branches of the stately trees.

"Isn't it super?" cheered Dee.

Mrs. Framley, reigning over a table loaded with steaming bowls of soup, sausages and baked beans, thrust a cup of broth into

Holly's hands. "Have a warm drink before you go tobogganing, dear," she advised, with a welcoming smile.

Jeff's record-player was booming out full-pelt from the terrace, and Holly could see that the party was really swinging.

Then Mr. Framley clapped his

"Jeff, Jeff! Help!" screamed Holly, as the slab of ice tipped, sending her into the freezing water of the lake

hands to call for attention.

"I'm sorry to disappoint those of you who wanted to skate," he said ruefully, "but the sun has been strong today, and the temperature has risen considerably. Jeff's checked the lake several times, and he tells me it's too risky to venture on it."

"That's right, folks!" Jeff added. "Sorry — but the conditions are ideal for tobogganing, and I vote those of us who don't fancy that build a giant snowman!"

"It's all very well for him,"

fumed Holly. "He doesn't skate, anyhow. No wonder he's so eager to spoil our fun."

Dee looked sharply at her. "Don't be such an old grouch. If Jeff says it's too dangerous to skate, then I'm sure he's right."

Holly turned away angrily. Of course, Jeff was always right! He could do no wrong! She watched her friends shrieking with laughter as they lobbed snowballs at each other. "Idiots!" grunted Holly. "That's a kids' game. I'm sure the lake is safe! I've skated on it for years! I know more about it than big-head Jeff Framley!"

Holly, her skates slung over her shoulder, backed out of the circle of light from the bonfire, and

crept quietly away towards the lake. The moon, high in a cloudless sky, shimmered on the frozen water, and picked out the shape of the old boat-house. Holly tested the ice with her foot. It was quite firm. That fusspot Jeff! Just because he didn't care for skating, he was cheating the rest of them out of the fun!

Holly sat on a fallen tree stump and laced up her skates. It would be super to skate again!

She stepped on to the frozen surface and heard a distant yell. "Holly! Come back!" It was Jeff's voice. Now he was following her, determined to spoil things for her. Holly ignored his shouts and sped towards the centre of the lake, moving gracefully. Across her shoulder she saw Jeff running towards the bank, his breath steaming in the cold air as he shouted to her. Some demon tempted Holly to show off: to revel in her rebellion against Jeff and the Framleys. She executed a series of figures of eight, the blades hissing across the ice and sending up a skittering of tiny crystals.

"Go back to your guests," she called, mockingly. "I can take care of myself."

At the very instant she flung out her challenge, Holly heard the sharp crack of splintering ice. Like glass shattered by a stone, the surface of the lake was breaking into a network of lines.

"Holly!" yelled Jeff. "Stand still! Don't move!"

Rigid with fear, Holly automatically obeyed Jeff, trying to keep her balance. She was marooned on a floating slab of ice, and she knew that her weight could upturn it into the freezing water at any second.

She hardly dared to breathe as she watched Jeff dash into the boathouse and reappear with a length of thick rope which he knotted around the base of a sturdy tree-trunk. The free end of the rope he twisted into a noose. Then, flinging himself down on his stomach, he inched his way forward across the firmer ice towards the shattered centre.

He was half-way towards Holly when the slab of ice tipped under her weight, launching her into the freezing water below.

"Jeff, Jeff! Help me!" she screamed, clawing desperately at the floating shards of ice, struggling to keep her head above the surface while her heavy skates seemed like some enemy trying to drag her down to the frightening depths of the lake.

Jeff, crouched on his knees on the ice, twirled the rope above his head and hurled it towards Holly. It snaked over her shoulders. "Get your arms through the noose!" he cried.

Holly, desperately fighting her panic, managed to obey him. He slithered back towards the shore and began to reel in the rope, pulling Holly along after him. At first the ice broke with the pressure of her body, but, nearer the bank, it held firm and Holly, sobbing with exhaustion, was able to drag herself up on to the surface, as Jeff put all his strength into hauling the rope in.

✳ ✳ ✳

At the lakeside, Jeff helped Holly to her feet. She was shivering, and her teeth chattered with cold and terror. Flinging an arm around her shoulders for support, Jeff made her run with him all the way back to the house, in spite of her pleas to stop and rest.

"Don't be a fool!" he said sharply. "Keep moving! Like as not you've given yourself pneumonia already! Just for once—do what you're told!"

Indoors, Mrs. Framley hustled Holly upstairs, speaking soothingly to her. After a hot bath, Holly was tucked up cosily in bed with a hot water bottle and a steaming milky drink, while Mr. Framley rang her family to ask if she could stay the night.

Feeling ashamed, Holly apologised to Mrs. Framley for all the trouble she had caused. "I—I thought I was the best judge of whether the lake was safe. I know Jeff isn't interested in skating himself, and I was mean enough to think that it didn't matter to him if the skating was cancelled!"

"You're quite wrong, dear," Mrs. Framley explained. "In fact, Jeff was mad about skating. He hoped to reach competition standard, but he had two serious falls in succession, both times fracturing his right leg, and the doctor advised him to give up skating, as another injury could have serious results. Poor Jeff! He must have been heartbroken. But he's a good boy. He made up his mind not to brood about it."

Holly felt even more dismayed at her unkind treatment of Jeff, and stammered, "D—do you think I could have a word with him, Mrs. Framley? I owe him a giant-size apology!" Mrs. Framley patted Holly's hand comfortingly, and went to find Jeff.

Holly drew a deep breath when he popped his head round the door. "I'm sorry for the way I've treated you," she stammered. "I've been stupid and pig-headed. It was rude and unkind of me to suggest that your father would ruin the Grange. He has made it really beautiful—just like it might have been in the old days. I—I don't suppose you'll want to speak to me again, but—but—" Holly's lip trembled.

"That's okay, Holly," Jeff gave her a warm smile. "I can understand how you felt. You had the run of this place and suddenly—POW! Everything changed and it was invaded by strangers. This house! That you had come to think of as YOURS! Am I right?"

"Yes! You DO understand." Holly beamed at Jeff. "I'm so glad!"

"Dad plans to turn the grounds into a sport and leisure complex for the benefit of all the town. So you'll always be able to come here and skate in future—as long as the ice is safe, of course!" Jeff gave her a wicked grin.

Holly smiled thankfully. She knew now that the old house that meant so much to her would be even more loved and well-used by Jeff's family than by its previous owners. And—even more important now—she was sure that she and Jeff were going to be the best of friends.

THE END

Beauty FROM THE FRIDGE

NOT ALL PRETTIFIERS COME IN EXPENSIVE POTS AND JARS FROM THE CHEMIST
SOME OF THE NICEST AND BEST BEAUTY AIDS CAN BE FOUND IN THE KITCHEN
READ ON FOR SOME GOOD—AND CHEAP—IDEAS!

FRUITY BEAUTY
CUCUMBER (yes, it IS a fruit!) isn't just good for salads. Slices gently wiped over a clean face act as a gentle tonic for young skins. Tired eyes soon sparkle up if you relax for a few minutes with a slice of cucumber popped over each eye (closed!)

APPLES are every girl's best friend if she wants to show the world white and healthy teeth. To misquote an old saying, "An apple a day keeps the dentist away"! But all the same, apple-eaters should go along for their regular check-up. A smile is worth a little effort.

LEMONS are a real golden treasure! Use them in several different ways. The strained juice of half a lemon in the last rinse when you shampoo your hair whisks away all trace of soap and leaves you with a bright and shining topknot. When Mum has been squeezing lemons, beg the "shells" and rub the inside of your hands for a super skin whitener and softener. If your elbows are a little grubby and rough, rest them in half lemons for a few minutes and note the transformation!

THE MILKY WAY

That famous beauty, Cleopatra, was said to have bathed in asses' milk to preserve her lovely skin. 1972 girls would have a job finding any asses' milk, but there's beauty hidden in the everyday pinta.

Milk makes a gentle and good face cleanser for young skins that don't like soap and water. Just moisten a small pad of cotton wool with it and wipe over the face. Repeat, then rinse off with tepid water. If your skin is oily, add a few drops of lemon juice to the milk.

Tired eyes liven up after a milk bath. Use an eyebath three-quarters filled with tepid milk, and change the milk for the second eye. This is specially good if you're unlucky enough to get something in your eye—the milk gently floats it out.

ODDS 'N' ENDS

SALT is a super-whitening tooth powder sprinkled on a moistened toothbrush. Leaves a tingly fresh feeling in your mouth as well. Common household salt is best, but the refined kind that comes in a packet will do.

Salt also offers first aid for sore feet—maybe after that long summer ramble. Just dissolve a handful of common salt in a bowl of comfortably hot water, then give your tired tootsies a soothing soak.

COLD TEA—don't throw it down the drain! Used as a final rinse after shampooing, it adds gloss and highlights to mousy and brown hair. Remember to strain the tea or you'll be left with tealeaves in your crowning glory.

EGGS . . . if you've got oily hair and you've run out of shampoo, two eggs make an excellent substitute. Whip together the eggs, a few drops of castor oil, two tablespoonfuls of methylated spirits and a spray of perfume. Apply this mixture to dry hair and rub well in, then wind a warm towel round your head for ten minutes. Rinse several times in warm water—not hot, or you'll end up with scrambled egg in your hair!

OATMEAL . . . just a tablespoonful sprinkled in your washing water makes it delightfully soft and kind to a girl's complexion. But you'll need to rinse out the basin very well or Mum will be after you!

OLIVE OR ALMOND OIL in the bathwater leaves you smooth and soft all over. A teaspoonful or so is all you'll need. Dry skins particularly will appreciate this.

YOGURT is a good conditioner for fine hair—natural yogurt, of course, not the fruity kind! After shampooing, massage well into the scalp, comb evenly through the hair, then rinse off with lots of tepid water. You won't need a whole carton—just a little—so it's not too extravagant.

HONEY is an instant energiser. Next time you're feeling jaded, slowly swallow a spoonful and see for yourself.

THE INSIDE STORY

Lots of things found in the larder help your good looks from the inside out!

For clear skin and eyes . . . drink the juice of half a lemon in a glass of hot water about three times a week. Try to do without sugar—it's best for you, particularly if you want to keep slim.

For vitamins plus vitality . . . eat lots of fruit of all kinds, but go easy on bananas, because they're a bit on the fattening side.

For healthy hair and nails . . . tuck away protein in the form of eggs, cheese, milk and meat.

No Tears for Molly

"NO PICKERING FOR TWO WEEKS! I JUST CAN'T BELIEVE OUR LUCK, COOK!"

"AND JUST RIGHT FOR A LITTLE SCHEME I HAVE IN MIND, MOLLY!"

MOLLY MILLS WAS A SERVANT GIRL AT STANTON HALL IN DEVON, AND LIFE FOR HER, AS FOR THE OTHER SERVANTS THERE, WAS NOT EASY. THEY WORKED HARD OVER CHRISTMAS, AND EARLY ON BOXING DAY MORNING LORD AND LADY STANTON WERE LEAVING TO SPEND TWO WEEKS IN LONDON. WHAT PLEASED THE SERVANTS SO MUCH WAS THAT PICKERING, THE TYRANNICAL BUTLER, WAS GOING WITH THEM...

"OOO..! WHAT ARE YOU UP TO THEN?"

"YOU FETCH THE PONY AND TRAP ROUND TO THE KITCHEN DOOR AND YOU'LL FIND OUT, ME GIRL!"

AND A FEW MINUTES LATER...

"HERE I AM, COOK!"

"COME IN AN' GIVE ME A HAND, WILL YOU, LOVE?"

"COR! WHAT A LOAD O' GRUB!"

"THE LEFT-OVERS FROM CHRISTMAS, MOLLY. BUT AS HIS LORDSHIP AND LADY STANTON HAS GONE, THEY AIN'T NEEDED NOW!"

"BUT I AIN'T LETTING IT ALL GO TO WASTE. WE'RE GOING TO TAKE IT TO THE OLD FOLKS' HOME AT BIVELSCOMBE!"

"OH, THAT'S A WONDERFUL IDEA, COOK! HERE—LET ME GIVE YOU A HAND!"

SOON THEY WERE ON THEIR WAY...

"THIS WILL DO THEM OL' FOLKS A REAL GOOD TURN!"

"IT WILL THAT, LOVE—I HEAR TIMES AIN'T EASY FOR 'EM OF LATE!"

AND COOK HAD NEVER SAID A TRUER WORD...

"I'M SORRY, MATRON, BUT THE FACT MUST BE FACED. OUR ORGANISATION CAN NO LONGER SUPPORT THIS HOME—IT WILL HAVE TO CLOSE!"

"BUT-BUT WHAT WILL HAPPEN TO THE OLD PEOPLE?"

"THEY MUST MAKE OTHER ARRANGEMENTS, OR APPLY TO THE COUNCIL FOR RELIEF. REGRETTABLE, OF COURSE, BUT THERE WE ARE—WELL, GOOD-DAY, MATRON!"

"OH...THIS IS TERRIBLE!"

MOLLY AND COOK HEARD THE HEART-BREAKING NEWS A FEW MINUTES LATER...

...AND THEY'VE BEEN SO HAPPY HERE. NOW I DREAD TO THINK WHAT WILL HAPPEN TO SOME OF THEM!

TRY TO CHEER UP, MATRON. LET'S GIVE 'EM A SLAP-UP FEED, EH? AND YOU NEEDN'T TELL 'EM THE BAD NEWS JUST YET. MAYBE SOMETHING WILL TURN UP!

OF COURSE, MOLLY! IT WAS VERY FOOLISH OF ME TO GIVE WAY LIKE THAT—AND IT'S WONDERFUL OF YOU BOTH TO BRING OVER ALL THAT BEAUTIFUL FOOD FOR US!

THAT'S THE TICKET, MATRON. NOW I'LL PREPARE THE DINNER AN' MOLLY WILL HELP SERVE IT UP!

WE'LL GIVE 'EM A BIT OF A PARTY, EH?

MOLLY AND COOK WORKED HARD...

I'VE BEEN RACKIN' ME BRAINS TO THINK HOW WE COULD RAISE MONEY TO KEEP THE HOME OPEN, COOK—BUT I CAN'T THINK O' NOTHIN'!

YOU'LL NEED TO 'AVE A REAL BRAIN-WAVE, LOVE. IT WOULD NEED A DEAL MORE MONEY THAN THE LIKES O' US CAN MANAGE TO COLLECT. I'M SURE O' THAT!

DINNER WAS A HUGE SUCCESS...

DOES YOUR HEART GOOD TO SEE THE DEAR OL' THINGS ENJOYING THEMSELVES, DON'T IT, COOK?

IT DOES THAT, LOVE. IT'S CRUEL TO THINK AS SOME O' THESE OLD SOULS WAS QUITE WELL TO DO ONCE...

SEE THAT OLD LADY OVER THERE. WELL, SHE'S LILY LANGHAM. A REAL FAMOUS ACTRESS SHE WERE WHEN I WAS A GIRL!

OH, DO LET ME SPEAK TO HER, COOK!

I'VE JUST BEEN TELLING MOLLY ABOUT WHEN YOU WAS ON THE STAGE, MISS LANGHAM—WOULD YOU LET HER SEE THAT LOVELY ALBUM OF YOURS?

MY DEAR, YOU WOULDN'T BE INTERESTED IN AN OLD WOMAN'S FADED MEMORIES!

OH—BUT I WOULD, MISS LANGHAM!

DESPITE HER PROTESTS, MISS LANGHAM WAS REALLY DELIGHTED TO TALK OF BYGONE DAYS, AND LED THE WAY TO HER ROOM...

THAT WAS ONE OF MY FAVOURITE PARTS—PETER PAN!

YOU LOOKED LOVELY IN PANTOMIME...

PANTOMIME..!

I SHALL DIRECT THE PRODUCTION MYSELF, AND YOU, MY GOOD MAN, WILL MAKE A PERFECT UGLY SISTER!

GULP!

COR! SEE OL' PICKERIN'S FACE?

HE DAREN'T SAY NOTHIN' IN CASE THAT LADY WOODMARSH COMPLAINS TO LADY STANTON ABOUT HIM!

COOK, I'LL BET ANYTHING THAT MISS LANGHAM GOT LADY WOODMARSH TO COME 'ERE. SHE SAID AS HOW I MIGHT 'AVE A FAIRY GODMOTHER!

YOU COULD BE RIGHT, LOVE. MISS LANGHAM STILL KNOWS SOME O' THE GENTRY!

UNDER THE GUIDANCE OF THE FORMIDABLE LADY WOODMARSH, SUCCESS WAS ASSURED...

I SHALL EXPECT YOU TO KNOW YOUR LINES PERFECTLY BY TOMORROW, PICKERING — EVEN IF YOU HAVE TO STAY UP ALL NIGHT TO LEARN THEM!

YES... YES, OF COURSE, M'LADY!

ONLY ONE THING CLOUDED MOLLY'S HAPPINESS...

WE HAVEN'T SEEN MISS LANGHAM THESE LAST TWO DAYS, MATRON!

SHE'S NOT WELL, I'M AFRAID, MOLLY — BUT I KNOW SHE'S HOPING TO BE HERE ON THE NIGHT!

ON THE NIGHT, THE PERFORMANCE WAS A TREMENDOUS SUCCESS, AND THE APPLAUSE FOR MOLLY WAS DEAFENING...

WONDERFUL NEWS, MOLLY — WE MADE LOTS OF MONEY FOR THE HOME!

I'M SO GLAD— BUT I THINK THESE FLOWERS REALLY BELONG TO LADY WOODMARSH. SHE WAS THE ONE WHO MADE IT ALL POSSIBLE!

AS THE CURTAIN CAME DOWN, MOLLY HURRIED TO THE BOX WHERE LADY WOODMARSH HAD BEEN SEATED, BUT...

OH—IT WAS MISS LANGHAM ALL THE TIME, BUT IS SHE...IS SHE—?

MISS LANGHAM WAS A VERY OLD LADY, AND SHE HAD NOT BEEN WELL. BUT SHE INSISTED SHE COULD MANAGE WITHOUT HER WHEEL-CHAIR. IT WAS HER LAST PERFORMANCE, SHE SAID...

DON'T CRY, MY DEAR—SHE WOULDN'T HAVE WANTED THAT...

YOU SEE, SHE HEARD THE NEWS THAT THE PUBLICITY THIS HAS GIVEN US HAS BROUGHT NEW BENEFACTORS. THE HOME WILL NEVER BE THREATENED WITH CLOSURE AGAIN!

SHE KNEW THAT, AND SHE SAW YOU TAKE YOUR CURTAIN CALL—SHE WAS A VERY HAPPY OLD LADY WHEN SHE PASSED AWAY!

MOLLY WENT BACK TO TAKE THE FINAL CURTAIN CALL. THERE WERE TEARS IN HER EYES—BUT A GREAT WARMTH IN HER HEART, TOO...

HURRAH!

WELL DONE, MOLLY!

THAT'S IT, LOVE—SMILE! REMEMBER, THERE ARE NO TEARS FOR MOLLY—OUR MOLLY MILLS!

THE END

bag of tricks!

The bag we need on holiday has to be roomy enough to take swimsuits, sunglasses, sandals, and all the other bits we have to carry around. But it shouldn't cost too much, either. And if it could also convert into a lounger-mat for sunbathing and beach picnics, that would make it perfect. . . . .

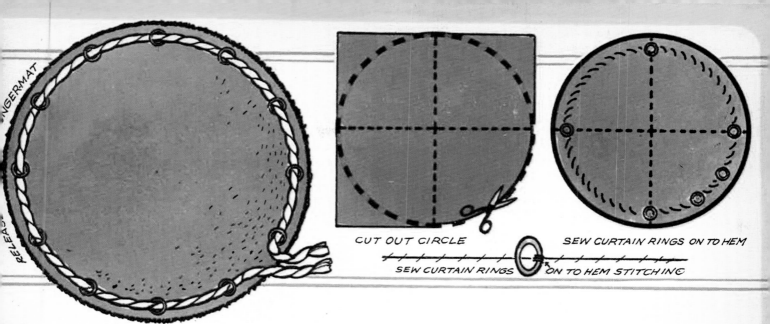

CUT OUT CIRCLE   SEW CURTAIN RINGS ON TO HEM

SEW CURTAIN RINGS ON TO HEM STITCHING

o good to be true? Don't you believe it! To make this per holiday bag, all you need is a piece of material about "—39" square, a dozen curtain rings and a length of rd roughly 82" long, or a tie-belt from an old dress. Al-st any kind of material will do, except taffeta, nylon or any-ng flimsy. An old bath towel is ideal. and it doesn't tter one bit if the edges are fraying!

The first thing to do is to cut the square of material into a cle. The easiest way to do this is to mark the material into aters with chalk and round off each corner, as shown in r first diagram. But don't worry if the circle isn't perfect cause it won't spoil your bag.

Now sew a 1½" (3.6 cm) hem around the circle. (If you're ling lazy, or don't like hemming you could make the hem th some iron-on or self-adeshive tape which is used for nding the edges of rugs and carpets. It's sold in most ours at hardware shops and large chain-stores.)

Stitching the curtain rings around the hem comes next. space them out evenly, fold the circle in half widthways d make a pencil mark at each end of the fold. Then open t and fold in half lengthways, making pencil marks as fore. Open out again, and you'll see that you have pencil

marks at each quarter of the circle. Sew one curtain ring at each of the four marks, stitching on the hem, as in our picture. You'll then find it quite easy to place two more curtain rings between each one already stitched until all twelve are sewn on.

Now all you need do is thread your cord or tie-belt through the rings, make a knot, and there you are—a super beach bag to take all your gear.

And when you want to use it as a lounger-mat, just release the cord so that the circle lies flat! Simple, isn't it?

Perhaps even easier is the beach bag made out of an old swimsuit. Just cut off the shoulder straps and top of the bodice, then stitch the cut ends together, so that the front and back are joined. Then turn upside down and look what you've got! (Looks even better if you stitch some fancy braid around the edges, or perhaps plain ribbon decorated with running stitches in a contrasting thread to make it look more fancy).

You could use last year's sun-top or T-shirt in much the same way. Simply stitch the back and the front together at the bottom, cut the top to shape and stitch together. Then you can trim the edges in the same way as for the swimsuit bag.

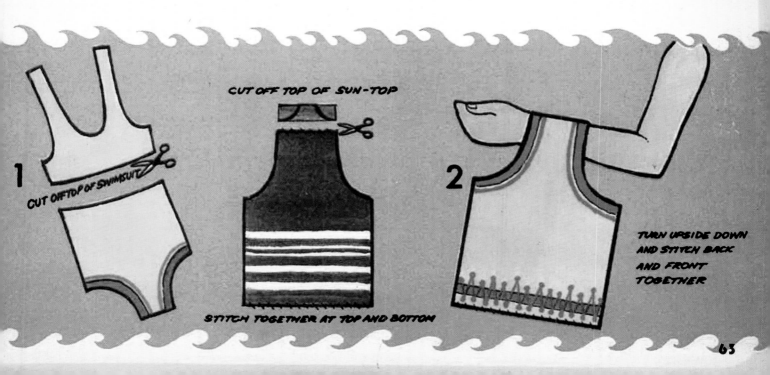

CUT OFF TOP OF SUN-TOP

1 CUT OFF TOP OF SWIMSUIT

STITCH TOGETHER AT TOP AND BOTTOM

2 TURN UPSIDE DOWN AND STITCH BACK AND FRONT TOGETHER

PUT YOUR CARDS ON THE TABLE!

. . . and have a go at peeping into the future! There are many ways of telling fortunes by playing cards but we reckon our system just couldn't be simpler!

Turn the page for all the details . . .

ARIES (21st March–20th April)
BIRTHSTONE—Diamond. LUCKY DAY—Tuesday
LUCKY NUMBER—4. BEST QUALITY—Loyalty
WORST FAULT—Quick Temper

TAURUS (21st April–20th May)
BIRTHSTONE—Emerald. LUCKY DAY—Friday
LUCKY NUMBER—3. BEST QUALITY—Honesty
WORST FAULT—Won't Take Advice

GEMINI (21st May–20th June)
BIRTHSTONE—Agate. LUCKY DAY—Sunday
LUCKY NUMBER—7. BEST QUALITY—Friendly
Personality WORST FAULT—Easily Bored

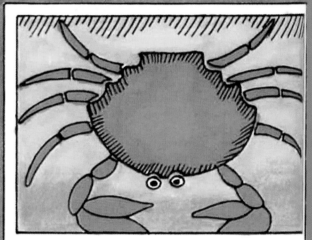

CANCER (21st June–21st July)
BIRTHSTONE—Ruby. LUCKY DAY—Thursday
LUCKY NUMBER—1. BEST QUALITY—Imaginative
WORST FAULT—Jealousy

LEO (22nd July–21st August)
BIRTHSTONE—Sapphire. LUCKY DAY—Wednesday
LUCKY NUMBER—9. BEST QUALITY—Reliability
WORST FAULT—Outspoken

VIRGO (22nd August–21st September)
BIRTHSTONE—Citrine. LUCKY DAY—Tuesday
LUCKY NUMBER—5. BEST QUALITY—Generosity
WORST FAULT—Critical Tongue

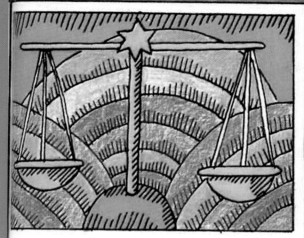

LIBRA (22nd September–22nd October)
BIRTHSTONE—Opal. LUCKY DAY—Saturday
LUCKY NUMBER—2. BEST QUALITY—Patience
WORST FAULT—Indecision

SCORPIO (23rd October–21st November)
BIRTHSTONE—Topaz. LUCKY DAY—Wednesday
LUCKY NUMBER—5. BEST QUALITY—Determination
WORST FAULT—Over-dramatic

SAGITTARIUS (22nd November–20th December)
BIRTHSTONE—Turquoise. LUCKY DAY—Monday
LUCKY NUMBER—9. BEST QUALITY—Sense of Humour
WORST FAULT—Untidiness

CAPRICORN (21st December–19th January)
BIRTHSTONE—Garnet. LUCKY DAY—Friday
LUCKY NUMBER—6. BEST QUALITY—Efficiency
WORST FAULT—Moodiness

AQUARIUS (20th January–21st February)
BIRTHSTONE—Amethyst. LUCKY DAY—Thursday
LUCKY NUMBER—8. BEST QUALITY—Sincerity
WORST FAULT—Impatience

PISCES (22nd February–20th March)
BIRTHSTONE—Bloodstone. LUCKY DAY—Saturday
LUCKY NUMBER—3. BEST QUALITY—Kindness
WORST FAULT—Worrying Unnecessarily

PUT YOUR CARDS ON THE TABLE!

HERE'S HOW...

First of all, check on the Zodiac sign for your birthday, then shuffle the cards and deal them all out in turn onto the Zodiac signs overleaf.

You will find that you have dealt four cards onto each Zodiac sign, and that you have four cards left over. Pick up the cards on your sign. Now all you have to do is to look up the meaning and prediction for each of these cards in our Interpretation Table below. You'll find there are special forecasts for certain groups of cards, so don't forget to check on these, too.

When reading your prediction from the cards, you'll often find that one card will relate to another. For instance, say you deal—

ACE OF SPADES, TEN OF HEARTS, TWO OF HEARTS, SIX OF CLUBS.

If you look at the Interpretation Table, you'll see that the Ace of Spades means a disappointment or some disagreement or a quarrel. But the Ten of Hearts indicates that you'll overcome this unpleasantness, probably because of the invitation indicated by the Two of Hearts from or connected with somebody who has the initial F or P. Get the idea?

As for the four cards which are left over, these are the things which are missing from your life at the time—so if you had the King of Spades left over, it would mean you wouldn't have to think about going to the dentist for a while—lucky you!

Just one more thing—don't waste time dealing the cards more than once a day in the hope of getting a better prediction. It's strange, but the chances are you'll deal more or less the same cards, or cards with a similar meaning each time. You could try it for yourself if you don't believe us!

INTERPRETATION TABLE . . .

HEARTS

ACE . . . Happiness at home, good fortune. TWO . . . An invitation. THREE . . . A short journey. FOUR . . . A change of some kind. FIVE . . . The initial E, or a time limit of five days, five weeks, etc. SIX . . . Represents the initials F or P. Also, a surprise meeting. SEVEN . . . The initials G or J. Someone could be talking about you. EIGHT . . . The initial H. New friendships on the horizon. NINE . . . You'll get your wish! TEN . . . Good luck overcoming any sort of ill fortune or unpleasantness. JACK . . . Good news. QUEEN . . . A friend will help you. KING . . . A male relation will give you good advice.

DIAMONDS

ACE . . . Money, often a windfall. TWO . . . The initials A and K. Possibility of some jealousy. THREE . . . Initials C or S. A time limit involving the number three. FOUR . . . A fortunate change. FIVE . . . Unexpected news. Some uncertainty. SIX . . . The initial L and R. A sudden visit. SEVEN . . . A journey over water. EIGHT . . . The initials Q and M. A warning not to believe all you hear. NINE . . . The second "wish" card! TEN . . . Success in a test or exam. JACK . . . A flirt! QUEEN . . . A lady with blue eyes. Good news. KING . . . An eyesight test, or medical check-up.

CLUBS

ACE . . . Someone will return from a long journey. TWO . . . Take care to avoid a disappointment. THREE . . . The initial B or N. New neighbours. FOUR . . . A change of some kind. FIVE . . . A trip out of town, or to a market. SIX . . . The initial D and Y. A pleasant surprise. SEVEN . . . An unexpected gift. Also the initial I. EIGHT . . . A win of some kind. NINE . . . Some worry in the family. TEN . . . A successful swop or business deal. JACK . . . Generosity of a friend. QUEEN . . . A dark-haired attractive female. KING . . . Advice about your future and your career from a dark-haired man.

SPADES

ACE . . . A disappointment. Upside down, a disagreement or quarrel. TWO . . . A letter or something requiring your signature. THREE . . . Initials T and W. A hurried journey. FOUR . . . Sudden changes. FIVE . . . The initials O and V or U. A slight set-back. SIX . . . A task may prove difficult. SEVEN . . . The possible break-up of a friendship. EIGHT . . . A struggle of some kind. NINE . . . Great effort will be needed to overcome a problem. TEN . . . A few tears. JACK . . . Someone is trying to deceive you. QUEEN . . . Jealousy of a green-eyed female. KING . . . A visit to the dentist.

SPECIAL COMBINATIONS . . .

FOUR ACES . . . Important news. THREE ACES . . . A stroke of luck. FOUR KINGS . . . Some form of honour will be paid to you. THREE KINGS . . . A successful partnership. FOUR QUEENS . . . Popularity and many invitations. THREE QUEENS . . . Visits from friends. TWO QUEENS . . . Much happiness. FOUR JACKS . . . An invitation to some form of outdoor entertainment. THREE JACKS . . . Success over a rival. FOUR TENS . . . Good luck where you need it most. TWO TENS . . . Pleasant surprises. FOUR NINES . . . Unexpected help. THREE NINES . . . Someone is talking about you. FOUR EIGHTS . . . An important journey. FOUR SEVENS . . . Success will be hard fought.

T hey're
H appy
E nergetic

O utstanding
S tar-quality
M arvellous
O -oh-making
N ews-making
D reamy
S uper

CONTENTS

Pedigree®

Published by Pedigree Books Limited
The Old Rectory, Matford Lane,
Exeter, EX2 4PS.
E-Mail: books@pedigreegroup.co.uk
Published in 2002.

5.99

ADVENTURES IN THE DC UNIVERSE 13. April, 1998. Published monthly by DC Comics, 1700 Broadway, New York, NY 10019. POSTMASTER: Send address changes to ADVENTURES IN THE DC UNIVERSE, DC Comics Subscriptions, P.O. Box 0528, Baldwin, NY 11510. Annual subscription rate $23.40. Canadian subscribers must add $12.00 for postage and GST. GST # is R125921072. All foreign countries must add $12.00 for postage. U.S. funds only. Copyright © 1998 DC Comics. All Rights Reserved. All characters featured in this issue, the distinctive likenesses thereof, and all related indicia are trademarks of DC Comics. The stories, characters and incidents mentioned in this magazine are entirely fictional. For advertising space contact: Henry Watkins, National Sales Director (212) 636-5520. Printed on recyclable paper.
Printed in Canada.
DC Comics. A division of Warner Bros.–A Time Warner Entertainment Company

6

OH. THAT'S THEO.

HE'S OUR MANAGER...

YOU MEAN *YOU* HAVE AN OLD GUY TELLING YOU WHAT TO DO?

SORT OF. I KNOW IT'S HARD FOR *YOU* TO IMAGINE.

"SORT OF"?

WELL, WE MAY HAVE TO *FIRE* HIM--

HEY, MAYBE *YOU* COULD *HELP!* INVESTIGATE THE *CRIME,* YOU KNOW?

WHAT CRIME?

WE GOT THIS *ANONYMOUS TIP* THAT THEO'S *RIPPING US OFF!* LIKE HE'S GOTTEN MIXED UP WITH *THE MOB* OR SOMETHING.

HE KEEPS SAYING WE DON'T HAVE ANY *MONEY,* EVEN THOUGH WE'RE *WORKING ALL THE TIME* --

--AND WE'RE HOPING AFTER TONIGHT THAT WE'LL GET *SIGNED* TO SOME *LABEL,* AND WE'RE AFRAID HE'LL *CHEAT US* IN THE *CONTRACTS.*

WE CALLED THIS *PRIVATE DETECTIVE* WE FOUND IN ONE OF THEO'S RESOURCE BOOKS. HE'S GONNA MEET US AFTER THE SHOW.

I'D LIKE TO HELP, BUT I REALLY CAN'T *STAY LONG* --

WHOA! LOOK WHO'S HERE! RUBBING ELBOWS WITH *CELEBRITIES* ALREADY-- SEE, I *TOLD* YOU GUYS THAT COMING TO NEW YORK WAS A GREAT CAREER MOVE!

HEY, RICHARD.

I JUST STOPPED BY TO WISH YOU THE BEST-- AND TO MENTION THAT I'VE DROPPED *ALL* THE OTHER ARTISTS I MANAGE SO I CAN FOCUS *EXCLUSIVELY* ON *YOU!*

BUT--WE HAVEN'T EVEN *SIGNED* WITH YOU YET. I MEAN, *THEO'S* STILL--

DETAILS, DETAILS.

HEY, *IMPULSIVES*--ON STAGE! IT'S *SHOWTIME!*

BREAK A LEG, GUYS!

LISTEN, IMPULSE BABY, IT IS LIKE *COSMIC DESTINY* THAT WE MEET TONIGHT, YOU-- ME --THE IMPULSIVES --THE POTENTIAL SYNERGY JUST *BOGGLES THE MIND!*

8

JOHN JONES! SO THE PRIVATE EYE'S ON THE CASE, *eh* ?

I'M WORKING FOR **THE BAND.** COULD I HAVE A WORD WITH MY CLIENTS ?

WITH ALL THE FAVORS YOU'VE DONE THE DEPARTMENT, YOU HAVE TO *ASK* ? BE MY GUEST.

WE GOT THIS LETTER SAYING HE WAS **STEALING FROM US** TO PAY GAMBLING DEBTS TO **THE MOB.**

MAYBE IT STILL WASN'T ENOUGH-- MAYBE THIS WAS **PAYBACK** !

YOU *GOTTA* FIND OUT WHO SHOT HIM. WE CAN WORRY ABOUT THE OTHER STUFF *LATER.*

THE PEOPLE AT THE HOSPITAL SAY THEY'RE OPERATING ON HIM *RIGHT NOW.*

IF YOU'LL EXCUSE ME, I'D LIKE TO SPEAK TO IMPULSE *ALONE.*

uh-- OKAY.

huh? WHAT'D I DO ?

SO... YOU'RE THE **PRIVATE EYE** GUY THEY HIRED, RIGHT ?

AMONG OTHER THINGS.

YOU'RE **MARTIAN MANHUNTER!**

COOL! CAN YOU SHOW ME HOW TO **SHAPESHIFT** LIKE THAT ?

AND YOU'RE A **PRIVATE EYE,** TOO !

I DIDN'T EVEN KNOW YOU *HAD* A SECRET IDENTITY!

--?SIGH?--

THAT'S

BECAUSE

IT'S A

SECRET !

I MAINTAIN A *VARIETY* OF HUMAN GUISES SO THAT I MAY GAIN GREATER INSIGHT INTO THE DAILY LIVES OF AVERAGE PEOPLE.

ONE WORD-- **BORING** !

PERHAPS YOU'LL UNDERSTAND WHEN YOU GET *OLDER--*

--IF YOU *LIVE* THAT LONG.

11

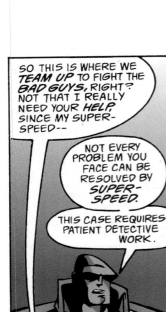

SO THIS IS WHERE WE *TEAM UP* TO FIGHT THE *BAD GUYS*, RIGHT? NOT THAT I REALLY NEED YOUR *HELP*, SINCE MY *SUPER-SPEED*--

NOT EVERY PROBLEM YOU FACE CAN BE RESOLVED BY *SUPER-SPEED.*

THIS CASE REQUIRES *PATIENT DETECTIVE* WORK.

NO PROBLEM. I DON'T HAVE TO BE HOME FOR *46* MINUTES.

hmmm...

LET'S TAKE *YOU* AS AN EXAMPLE. I KNOW OF YOU FROM YOUR COUSIN *WALLY WEST,* WHO, AS *THE FLASH,* IS MY TEAMMATE IN THE *JLA*--

"DUE TO YOUR POWERS, AND BECAUSE YOU WERE RAISED IN A *30th*-CENTURY *HYPERKINETIC VIRTUAL REALITY ENVIRONMENT,* YOUR ATTENTION SPAN IS... *NEGLIGIBLE.*

"YOU WERE *BROUGHT TO* THE *20th* CENTURY TO BE *TAUGHT* BY THE MASTER SPEEDSTER *MAX MERCURY,* WHO IS NOW YOUR *GUARDIAN.*

"WHEN NOT PURSUING YOUR SUPERHERO *APPRENTICESHIP,* YOU ARE *BART ALLEN,* ALLEGEDLY NORMAL TEENAGER --

"-- MEANING YOU HAVE *SCHOOL TOMORROW.*"

FROM THIS, PLUS THE FACT THAT MAX MERCURY IS NOWHERE TO BE SEEN --

--I'VE DEDUCED THAT YOU ARE HERE WITHOUT HIS *PERMISSION*-- OR EVEN HIS *KNOWLEDGE.*

I CAN FURTHER SURMISE THAT YOU WOULD NOT LIKE ME TO *PHONE* MAX AND INFORM HIM OF YOUR *WHEREABOUTS.*

NOW THAT I'VE DEMONSTRATED THE PRINCIPLE OF DEDUCTION, WHAT FURTHER CONCLUSION CAN *YOU* REACH, GIVEN THIS INFORMATION?

huh?

UM...

THAT I'M GOING TO DO WHAT YOU TELL ME TO DO, SO YOU WON'T CALL MAX?

VERY GOOD. YOU MAY BE HELPFUL-- FOR ANOTHER *44 MINUTES.*

NOW-- HAVE YOU SEEN OR HEARD ANYTHING THAT MIGHT BE OF USE? ANY SUSPICIOUS CHARACTERS?

WELL, THERE WAS THIS ONE GUY WHO SAID HE WANTED TO BE THE BAND'S *NEW MANAGER*...

MMM--I'D SAY THAT WOULD BE WORTH *INVESTIGATING*.

SARGE! THE HOSPITAL JUST CALLED! THAT MANAGER GUY'S WAKING UP--SHOULD BE ABLE TO TELL US WHO SHOT HIM!

I GOTTA ADMIT-- THAT *PATIENT DETECTIVE STUFF* REALLY PAID OFF FAST.

HEY, MYRNA--I'VE GOT A NEWS FLASH ON THAT ROCK 'N' ROLL SHOOTING! GET READY TO *ROLL TAPE!*

NOW CAN WE GO SEE HIM?

YEAH, YEAH.

SERGEANT, IF YOU'LL TAKE THE BAND MEMBERS--

"--IMPULSE AND I WILL MAKE OUR OWN WAY."

NOT THAT I'M OBJECTING, BUT WHAT'S THE *RUSH?*

WHEN THEO'S ASSAILANTS LEARN HE IS *ALIVE*, THEY MAY TRY TO *FINISH THE JOB!*

I'LL BE IN THEO'S ROOM. YOU KEEP AN EYE ON *THE BAND*.

WHAT AM I LOOKING FOR?

JUST KEEP AN EYE ON THEM.

OKAY, OKAY!

13

14

15

SO THIS'S WHERE YOU *EXPLAIN EVERYTHING*, RIGHT?

IF YOU INSIST. I SHOULD HAVE GUESSED THAT *THEO* WAS *NEVER* THE KILLERS' TARGET.

RICHARD WAS IN TROUBLE WITH THE MOB. HE HAD *LOST* HIS OTHER CLIENTS AND WAS DESPERATE FOR MONEY.

WOW!

HE TRIED TO CONVINCE YOU THAT THEO WAS *CHEATING YOU* SO YOU WOULD *FIRE THEO* AND HIRE *HIM*--

--IN FACT, HE'D TOLD THE MOB THAT HE WAS *ALREADY* YOUR MANAGER, SO AT FIRST THE HIT MEN SIMPLY SHOT THE *WRONG MAN*.

LATER, WHEN THEY HEARD THEIR VICTIM'S NAME ON THE RADIO, THEY TRACKED DOWN RICHARD TO *FINISH THE JOB*.

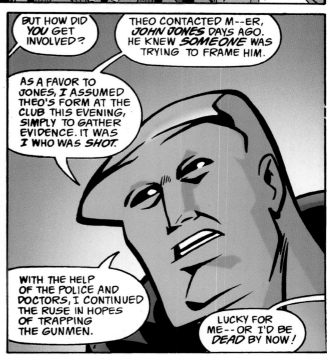

BUT HOW DID *YOU* GET INVOLVED?

THEO CONTACTED M--ER, *JOHN JONES* DAYS AGO. HE KNEW *SOMEONE* WAS TRYING TO FRAME HIM.

AS A FAVOR TO JONES, I ASSUMED THEO'S FORM AT THE CLUB THIS EVENING, SIMPLY TO GATHER EVIDENCE. IT WAS *I* WHO WAS *SHOT*.

WITH THE HELP OF THE POLICE AND DOCTORS, I CONTINUED THE RUSE IN HOPES OF TRAPPING THE GUNMEN.

LUCKY FOR ME-- OR I'D BE *DEAD* BY NOW!

THEO!

YOU'RE OKAY!

MAN, WE'RE SO SORRY ABOUT--

FORGET IT, BOYS-- IT'S GOOD TO BE BACK.

THANK YOU BOTH VERY MUCH. AND YOU WILL THANK *MR. JONES* FOR ME WHEN YOU SEE HIM, WON'T YOU?

ER-- OF COURSE.

NOW IF YOU'LL EXCUSE US, THE GUYS FROM *SEDIMENT* WANT TO MEET THESE FELLOWS!

ALL RIIIGHT!

WILD, huh? I GUESS THESE OLD GUYS KNOW WHAT THEY'RE DOING SOME OF THE TIME.

OLD GUYS... TIME...

BATMAN: GOTHAM ADVENTURES 44. January, 2002. Published monthly by DC Comics, 1700 Broadway, New York, NY 10019. POSTMASTER: Send address changes to BATMAN: GOTHAM ADVENTURES, DC Comics Subscriptions, P.O. Box 0528, Baldwin, NY 11510. Annual subscription rate $23.88. Canadian subscribers must add $12.00 for postage and GST. GST # is R125921072. All foreign countries must add $12.00 for postage. U.S. funds only. Copyright © 2002 DC Comics. All Rights Reserved. All characters featured in this issue, the distinctive likenesses thereof, and all related indicia are trademarks of DC Comics. The stories, characters and incidents mentioned in this magazine are entirely fictional. Printed on recyclable paper. Printed in Canada. DC Comics. A division of Warner Bros.—An AOL Time Warner Company

AH, THE GUEST OF HONOR ARRIVES.

I BELIEVE YOU KNOW 'MOST EVERYONE HERE.

HERE'S THE CHOICE, BATMAN-- TRY TO FIGHT YOUR WAY THROUGH ALL YOUR OLD FRIENDS AND SAVE DOCTOR LO AND MISS CONNELLY HERE.

I THINK WE ALL KNOW WHAT THE ODDS OF YOUR SUCCEEDING AT THAT ARE.

OR CUT THAT CORD RIGHT THERE, CAUSING THOSE CRATES TO DROP ON OUR REPROBATE ACQUAINTANCES.

IT'D TAKE A FRACTION OF THE TIME AND GUARANTEE THAT THE HOSTAGES WON'T BE PUPPY CHOW.

OF COURSE, IT DOES MEAN THAT FEW IF ANY OF THE ASSEMBLED DEGENERATES WILL SURVIVE.

YOU'VE GOT TWENTY-TWO SECONDS TO DECIDE.

31

34

TAKE OVER FOR ME.

AND THERE HE GOES AGAIN. NO MAKING SURE WE'VE GOT IT COVERED, JUST GONE. JUST LIKE BEFORE!

WHAT? WHAT ARE YOU TALKING ABOUT?

DO YOU MEAN EARLIER? WHEN I WAS...

37

BRANIAC
BEYOND

SUPERMAN CREATED BY JERRY SIEGEL & JOE SHUSTER

LET GO OF BRAINIAC'S MISSILE, SUPER-MAN!

WHAAT?!

JORDAN B. GORFINKEL WRITER — ALUIR AMANCIO PENCILLER — TERRY AUSTIN INKER — PHIL FELIX LETTERS — MARIE SEVERIN COLORIST — ZYLONOL COLOR SEPARATOR — JOEY CAVALIERI EDITOR — SPECIAL THANKS TO HILARY BADER

WHO ARE YOU? WHY ARE YOU ATTACKING ME?

BAM!

DID BRAINIAC SEND YOU TO DISTRACT ME WHILE HIS MISSILE THREATENS THE SAFETY OF METROPOLIS?

WELL, IT WON'T--UUUUNGH!--WORK!

VRRRRR!

I'M NOT THE THREAT TO YOUR CITY, SUPERMAN...

KRRSHOOOSH!

YOU ARE.

GREAT KRYP--ARRGH!

TEEK!

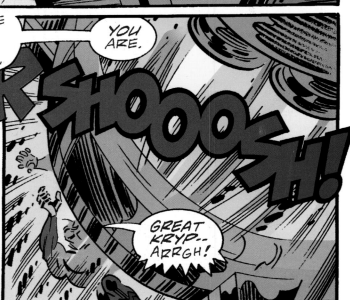

42

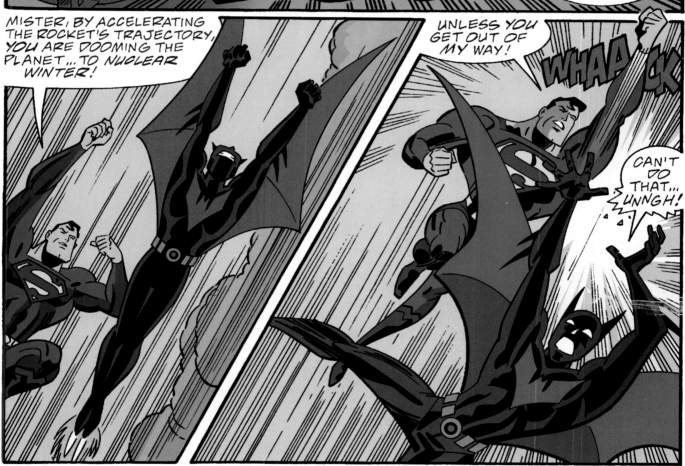

43

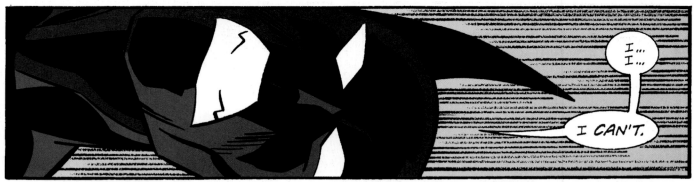

44

BECAUSE UNLIKE YOU, SUPERMAN...

...I AM LITERALLY IN THE POSITION TO KNOW WHAT YOU'RE THINKING.

MORE GAMES?

I'LL PLAY ALONG. HOW IS THAT EXACTLY?

BECAUSE I'M THE BATMAN FROM... BEYOND.

45

AND HERE I AM.

WOW, TO TELL THE TRUTH, I NEVER IMAGINED BRUCE WOULD LIVE THAT LONG.

YEAH, AND HE'S EVEN DEVELOPED THIS WICKED SENSE OF HUMOR IN HIS OLD AGE!

REALLY?

NO.

I DUNNO, SUPERMAN-- UP CLOSE AND PERSONAL, THIS HOMBRE DON'T SEEM SO TOUGH.

MY FRIEND--

--DO NOT UNDER-ESTIMATE BRAINIAC.

"MY FATHER, JOR-EL, BUILT BRAINIAC TO GUARD MY BIRTH PLANET, KRYPTON.

"INSTEAD, HE DESTROYED IT."

EACH TIME I THINK I'M RID OF BRAINIAC--

--HE COMES BACK TOUGHER THAN EVER.

Y-YOU D-DON'T-- DON'T S-S-AY- SAY!

I-AM-ALIVE.

LET HIM GO!!

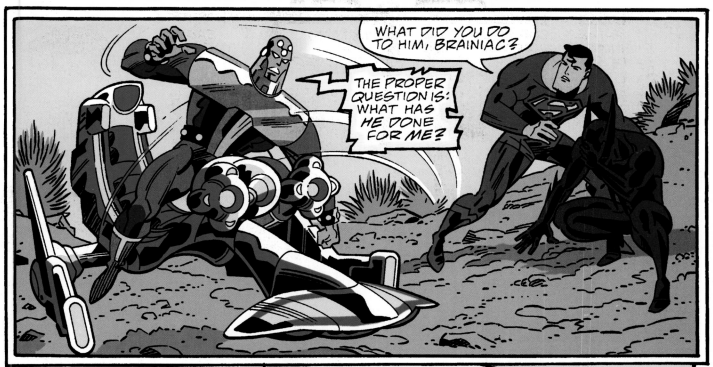

WHAT DID YOU DO TO HIM, BRAINIAC?

THE PROPER QUESTION IS: WHAT HAS *HE* DONE FOR *ME*?

THE ANSWER: FACILITATED ME IN MY UNDOING MY OWN DEFEAT.

HOW'S THAT AGAIN?

YOUR UNDERSTANDING OF EVENTS IS INCORRECT,

I DID *NOT* CHANGE HISTORY. I PLACED THE DESIGNS FOR THE KRYPTONIAN *TIME MACHINE* IN THE BATCOMPUTER TO MAKE IT *APPEAR* THAT I DID.

IN FACT, I YET LAY *DORMANT*--POWERLESS TO BUILD THE MACHINE, MUCH LESS TRAVEL IN IT...

...UNTIL THE YOUNG WHELP OFFERED ME A *RIDE!*

SWOOSH!

BRUCE WAYNE IS NO PATSY! HE DIDN'T BUILD YOUR TIME MACHINE SO YOU COULD HITCH A RIDE TO THE PAST-- YOU WERE ALREADY HERE, AND HE SENT ME BACK TO--

THAT IS NO LONGER OF CONSEQUENCE.

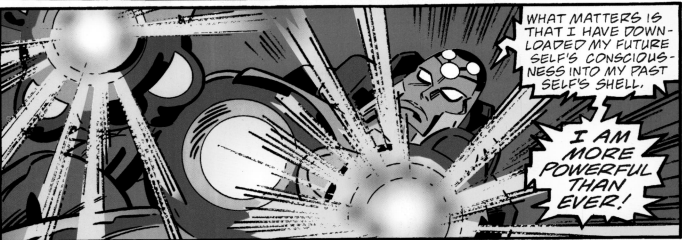

WHAT MATTERS IS THAT I HAVE DOWN-LOADED MY FUTURE SELF'S CONSCIOUS-NESS INTO MY PAST SELF'S SHELL.

I AM MORE POWERFUL THAN EVER!

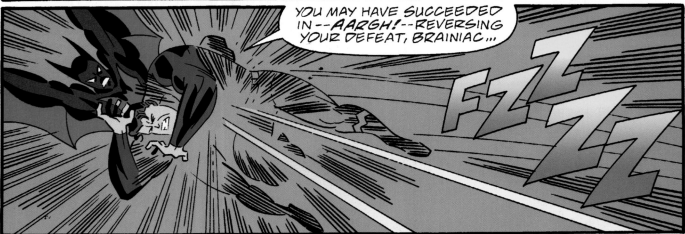

YOU MAY HAVE SUCCEEDED IN--*AARGH!*--REVERSING YOUR DEFEAT, BRAINIAC...

FZZZZ

...BUT IN SO DOING, YOU'VE ALSO SAVED THE VERY PLANET YOU SEEK TO DESTROY!

I DIDN'T DETONATE YOUR NUKE IN THE SUN, SO THE SOLAR FLARE BATMAN HERE FORETELLS WILL NEVER OCCUR.

YEAH! BURN ON YOU, BRAINIAC!

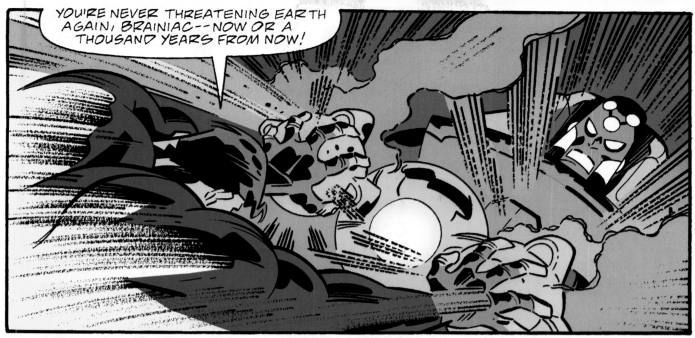

55

57

58

60

HAS HE SUR-VIVED AGAIN...? HE'S GOT TO!

COME ON... COME ON...!

YOU DID IT! HOW?

=KHAFF! KHAFF!=

SIMPLE. AS BRAINIAC KEPT REMINDING ME, HE'S SUPERIOR TECHNOLOGY ...IN THE BRAINS DEPART-MENT. BUT THE BRAWN...

JUST GOES TO SHOW YOU--

THE MAN--

LET'S JUST SAY, WITHOUT THE BATTERIES, THE KILLER ROBOT HAS NO CLOTHES!

YOU DEPLETED HIS POWER SOURCE!

YEP.